CW00664718

BRITISH
HORSE AND
PONY BREEDS
– and their future

BRITISH HORSE AND PONY BREEDS

– *and their future*

CLIVE RICHARDSON

J.A. ALLEN
LONDON

© Clive Richardson 2008
First published in Great Britain 2008

ISBN 978 0 85131 946 9

J.A. Allen
Clerkenwell House
Clerkenwell Green
London EC1R 0HT

J.A. Allen is an imprint of Robert Hale Limited

www.halebooks.com

The right of Clive Richardson to be identified as author
of this work has been asserted by him in accordance
with the Copyright, Designs and Patents Act 1988

A catalogue record for this book is available from the British Library

Photographs by, or property of, the author, except for those on page 203 by Nigel Apperley; on
pages 11, 18 (lower), 127 and 185 by Sue Baker; on page 121 by Judith Bean-Calhoun; on pages
116 and 190 by Jennifer Buxton; on page 183 by Thomas Capstick; on pages 125 and 199 by
Keith Curtis; on page 99 by Peter Dallow; on pages 84, 90 and 91 by Annie Dent; on page 132
(middle) by www.esphotography.co.uk; on page 96 by The Irish Draught Horse Society; on
pages 10 and 112 by Di Johnston; on page 155 by The Parachute Regiment; on pages 122, 199
and 200 by Alma Swan; on pages 104 and 135 by Richard Weller-Poley

Design by Judy Linard
Edited by Martin Diggle

Printed by New Era Printing Co. Limited, Hong Kong

ACKNOWLEDGEMENTS

I would like to thank the National Pony Society and the individual British breed societies, as well as Sue Baker, Jennifer Buxton, Judith Bean-Calhoun, Thomas Capstick, Nigel Cowgill, Keith Curtis, Peter Dallow, Annie Dent, Norma Grubb, Di Johnston, John Robinson, David Sykes, Alma Swan and Shirley Young for their assistance in providing information and illustrations which helped greatly in the production of this book.

CONTENTS

Chapter 1

EARLY ORIGINS

The horse is God's gift to Man.
Arab Saying

PRIMITIVE ANCESTORS OF THE HORSE

Upwards of 50 million years ago, the earliest recognizable ancestor of the horse, Eohippus, could be found browsing the soft vegetation in the primeval forests of what is now North America. Named from the Greek *eos* meaning dawn and *hippus* meaning horse, it stood no more than 12 in (30 cm) high, with an arched back, hindquarters higher than its shoulders, a long, thick tail and a snout-like muzzle. Its toes, four on the front feet and three on the back, had thickened claws like tiny hooves and it walked on dog-like pads. Its teeth were those of an animal which browsed on shrubs and undergrowth and were totally unsuited to grazing, and it lived alone or in small groups, its partially striped colouring giving it some camouflage from predators.

Although the discovery of fossil remains of Eohippus at Studd Hill in Kent in 1839 provided indisputable evidence that it had existed in Britain at one time, the archaeologists who unearthed its bones from the gravel pits where they had lain dormant for millennia did not recognize them as belonging to an early ancestor of the horse and named them after an entirely different species. The discovery of a more complete skeleton of Eohippus in America in 1876 enabled scientists to make detailed comparisons and ultimately agree that they were, in fact, one and the same – although they were unable to ascertain why Eohippus had died out in Europe. It is, therefore, to their ancestors from North America that all British horse and pony breeds ultimately owe their origins. Low sea levels had provided land bridges between North America, Asia, mainland Europe and the British Isles, and Eohippus and its descendants were able to travel freely over millions of years across what is now the Bering Straits and on into Asia and Europe, evolving continuously into an animal of more horse-like appearance as time passed.

Charles Darwin believed that the evolutionary process was one of natural selection whereby, when characteristics which are advantageous to a species manifest themselves in individuals, those animals are more likely to survive, prosper and breed. Thus the appearance of grasses around 25 million years ago saw Eohippus begin a gradual process of change, evolving from a forest browser to a grazer on the open expanses as it took advantage of the higher nutritional content and greater abundance of the new food source. It developed successfully by growing bigger, stronger and faster, with longer legs and a longer back, as it turned to speed rather than camouflage to escape from its predators. Also, its teeth developed into biting incisors and grinding molars to graze and chew the coarse grasses. The jaws deepened to accommodate the larger teeth with a longer and broader muzzle, and the eyes moved back on the head to permit better all-round vision as these primitive horses, now living in herds in the open, were more vulnerable to attack away from the safety of the forest. It is also likely that the striped markings once needed for forest camouflage began to fade over many generations as their function became obsolete on open grassland.

By around 6 million years ago, Pliohippus, as this evolved early horse is called, had migrated and spread across Eurasia before eventually and inexplicably dying out in America just as Eohippus had done earlier in Europe. Now much closer in appearance to the horse as we know it, the pads had gone from the feet and the side toes had virtually disappeared as the single hoof had developed. To enable it to graze even more efficiently, the teeth had become larger, with broader crowns.

Over the next 5 million years, Pliohippus was to split into the three family groups we know today as *Equus caballus* (from which all horse and pony breeds are descended), asses (including onagers) and zebras. *Equus Caballus* had one distinct advantage over its relations as it could adapt to living successfully in extremes of conditions, including variations in climate, terrain and vegetation, which the asses and zebras could not do, and this played a significant part in enabling it to colonize most parts of the world and develop into so many different types. As these early horses encountered a diversity of habitats from upland pastures to swampy forests, tundra and desert, the evolutionary process saw them develop into further sub-types, all of which played a role in the development of the British horse and pony breeds. Professor J. Cossar Ewart, in his book *The Multiple Origins of Horses and Ponies*, published in 1904, expressed the view that 'several species of horses inhabited Europe during the later portion of the Palaeolithic period', probably having quite a wide distribution, and three types in particular have been identified – Przevalski's horse, the Tarpan and the Diluvial (or Forest) horse.

Przevalski's horse, described by Lydekker in 1912 as 'intermediate in character between the horse on the one hand and kiang and onager on the other', once roamed throughout Asia and parts of Europe, and was the 'dun-coloured and more or less striped' ancestor of the horse that Darwin wrote about. The zoologist J. S. Poliakov named them after Colonel Nikolai M. Przevalski, an officer in the Imperial Russian Army, who first saw herds of them on the edge of the Gobi desert in 1879. Local Kirghiz tribesmen, who hunted them for meat, presented Przevalski with the skull and hide of one, which he donated to the St. Petersburg Zoological Museum. Przevalski's horse is probably the only true wild horse still in existence, surviving in small numbers in the wild – although there are captive herds breeding successfully in many zoological parks around the world.

Standing between 12 and 14 hands (122 and 142 cm), Przevalski's horse is a stocky animal with the large head and broad forehead characteristic of primitive horses. Przevalski himself thought the large head housed an equally large brain, indicating superior intelligence, and Colonel Hamilton Smith, an English naturalist and traveller, who wrote an article about these primitive horses in a leading natural history publication nearly 200 years ago, also commented on their alleged intelligence. The neck is short and strong with rather low withers, and the body is carried on relatively short legs. Colour ranges from a yellowish grey to mousy dun, with lighter colouring on the belly, muzzle and around the eyes, and a black dorsal stripe runs down the back from mane to tail. The dark brown or black mane is short and erect, with virtually no forelock, and the tail is black, merging into the body colour on the dock. The legs show indistinct transverse stripes, a legacy of forest-dwelling forebears, which are most clearly seen on the backs of the knees, and an indistinct stripe across the shoulders, generally a little darker than the rest of the body, can usually be discerned. It is quite probable that these Steppe horses were, at one time, found in Britain, as a decorated jawbone excavated in north Wales in 1880 appears to belong to a horse of Przevalski type, and fossilized bones found in caves in the Mendips again correspond to this type. Whether they remained in Britain, migrated back to what is now mainland Europe, or simply died out, is uncertain, but the Steppe horse undoubtedly had some influence in the development of some of the British breeds. However, it was the other two sub-species, the Tarpan and Diluvial or Forest horse, that contributed most.

The Tarpan was originally indigenous to southern Russia and eastern Europe, and was first described in any detail by Gmelin, a Russian naturalist, who came across a group of Tarpans near Voronesh in the spring of 1769. He recalled them as small, mouse-coloured horses with ash-grey bellies and black legs, noting that the head was 'thick', with long, pointed ears not unlike those of an ass. He also added that they were fast and extremely frightened of noise, implying that the characteristics of the open grassland grazer were implicit in these animals. Heptner, the Russian zoologist, and Pruski, the Polish scientist, conducted research to establish how the Tarpan differed from Przevalski's horse and found that, as well as being smaller and less robust than its Steppe cousin, the Tarpan had a narrower muzzle, smaller teeth and a finer, slightly dished face, with no paler colouring around the muzzle. However, the Tarpan retained the dark dorsal stripe, although the black mane was not upright and often fell to one side. Colonel Hamilton Smith was told by Cossacks in 1814 that the wild Tarpans of eastern Europe were predominantly mouse-grey, but many had interbred with domesticated horses. These hybrids rarely retained their original wild colour, and Heptner believed that between the territories of true Tarpans and Przevalski horses there existed interbred hybrid populations. With the loss of natural habitat, and domestic animals competing with the wild horses for grazing, the remaining pure-bred Tarpans were gradually pushed to extinction or absorbed into the domesticated horse population. The last Tarpan outside of Russia was killed in Lithuania in 1814, although the breed survived in Russia up until 1918 when the last true Tarpan died on an estate in Dumbrowska in the Ukraine.

The Tarpan was the direct ancestor of the wild pony of western Europe, which formed the main foundation stone for all British breeds as well as many other breeds across Europe. It is therefore interesting to note that in 1932 a German zoologist, Professor Lutz Heck, noticed that Koniks, which were the working ponies of the Polish peasants, occasionally bred a mouse-grey foal closely resembling the extinct Tarpan in type and colour. He began experimenting, using Przevalski stallions on Konik mares, to try to recreate a modern version of the Tarpan. At the same time, Professor Vetulani of Poznan University was involved in a similar project. According to Professor Janikowski, writing in 1942, the Konik's ancestors lived in a wild state in the great forest of Bialowieza in Poland until the eighteenth century, when some of them were brought into Count Zamoyski's private zoological park near Bilgoraj. At the beginning of the nineteenth century, during a particularly severe winter, the wild horses were captured and distributed among the local villagers, who tamed them and crossed them with their domesticated ponies – although a considerable number of them are alleged to have retained the pure blood of their wild ancestors. Clearly, the Konik pony of Poland was genetically not far removed from its Tarpan ancestry, and many scientists and zoologists believe that the present-day Exmoor pony is probably not far removed from the wild ponies portrayed in the cave paintings from Lascaux in the Dordogne region of France, dating from between 15,000 and 20,000 years ago. In theory, a point must be reached in all species when the animal is so well adapted to its environment, provided that environment is not subject to change itself, that further evolutionary development is unnecessary. In the case of Europe's wild ponies, that stage had most probably been reached quite some time ago.

There was, however, a third type of horse, which had evolved for living in a completely different type of terrain and which would also play a significant role in the development of British breeds. Central Europe had considerable areas of thick forest or partially wooded swamp and the adaptable horse soon colonized this terrain. To survive successfully in this alien environment it needed to reinvest in itself those characteristics needed by its earliest ancestors but discarded on its evolutionary journey. The Forest horse no longer relied on speed to escape its predators and, to afford better camouflage, its colour gradually darkened to brown or even black – although some zoologists believe it may have shown some striping to parts of its body, or possibly paler-coloured spots like a roe deer. Now surviving by concealment rather than flight, it grew and developed large, broad hooves to enable it to travel over soft ground more easily, and its temperament was likely to be passive in comparison to the flighty, tense nature of its grazing relatives. There is also evidence to suggest that its range of vision narrowed as it adapted for forest browsing again rather than grazing, and it probably lived alone or in small groups again as its environment was ill-suited for a herd existence. In the cave of Combarelles (like Lascaux, also in the Dordogne), there is the painted representation of a horse of much heavier and coarser build than those of Lascaux that we can identify as a Diluvial or Forest horse, and bones of these animals have been excavated in the south-east of England – although there is no evidence to suggest that they survived here after what is now the English Channel flooded at the end of the Ice Age.

The wild pony of western Europe, sometimes erroneously called the Celtic pony, while descended from the Tarpan, had evolved as a mountain pony suited to living and grazing on upland pastures. It had survived the Ice Age when, over a time-span of around 600,000 years, temperatures dropped to such an extent that the Arctic ice cap spread gradually south as far as the present site of London, driving all grazing animals before it as it completely covered the landscape, making it impossible to graze. Any animals that were cut off soon perished, and many species of grazing animals died out altogether. The ice, believed in places to be nearly a mile (1.6 km) deep, advanced and retreated at least four times, retreating for the last time around 10,000–12,000 years ago.

There is a widely held theory, supported by scientific research, that during the Ice Age an enclave formed in the larger part of northern Europe, where ponies as well as other mammals survived until the ice eventually began to thaw, and fossilized bones and teeth found on the site of the enclave would seem to provide supporting evidence. In these conditions only the hardiest ponies survived, grazing alongside mammoths and woolly rhinoceros and often falling prey to cave lions, bears and sabre-tooth tigers, not to mention Man, who left plenty of evidence that horse meat was a staple of his diet. Excavated horse bones from the sites of early settlements clearly show cuts made by flint knives, while the predominance of horse bones in relation to those of other animals points to these early hunters being selective in their prey.

The European pony was not the only sub-type descended from the Tarpan in Eurasia, but most sub-types became extinct or were merged into other types as time went on. Although the term 'horse' has been used generically in describing all these animals, in adapting to survive the harsh winters and poor vegetation they evolved certain characteristics such as small ears to preserve body warmth, which we now regard as essentially 'pony'. However, the term 'pony' was a much later appellation, the origins of which are obscure. The Reverend John Brand, writing in 1701, described Shetland ponies as 'a sort of little horses called Shelties', and in Tudor times Henry VIII's laws and statutes referred to animals of less than 13 hands (132 cm) as 'horses', while Samuel Johnson, in his much-quoted dictionary of 1755, concluded: 'I know not the origin of this word, unless it be corrupted from puny.' A possible explanation is that the word is of Scottish origin and derived from the French word '*poulain*', meaning a foal, French being the second language of the Scottish upper classes during the Stuart era. Alternatively, it could be derived from the Scottish word 'pow', meaning the poll, as the area around the poll, including the small ears, is generally acknowledged to be an indication of pony character. Significantly, the first recorded spelling of the word was 'powney'. W. J. Miles, writing in 1865, when the word 'pony' had come into more general use, commented: 'Owing, however, to the large stature of the English horse, anything under thirteen hands has, in horseman's phrase, come to be called "a pony".' Today, the delineation between a horse and a pony is almost invariably based on size only, rather than on characteristics.

BRITISH DEVELOPMENTS AFTER THE ICE AGE

Following the Ice Age, over the next few thousand years temperatures slowly began to rise, melting the ice caps and raising the level of the seas until, between 7,000 and 8,000 years ago, the English Channel flooded, giving Britain its island status. Unable to travel across the marshy stretch of ground between Britain and mainland Europe in search of better grazing (or to avoid predators including Man, who was still hunting the ponies as a favoured source of food but whose hunting skills were now far more advanced), the British ponies were marooned. With no way of introducing new blood without Man's intervention, the scene was set for the development of the British native horse and pony breeds.

The milder, wetter weather which came to characterize the British climate at that time also began to produce different types of terrain, from heathland to boggy lowlands, dense forests and open, scrubby woodland. The ponies gradually populated these habitats, migrating in seasonal cycles or to avoid the depredations of hunters, and initiating the first steps on the next stage of their evolutionary path as they began to adapt to the different environments found within the British islands. In the Shetlands, Orkneys, Hebrides and other northerly Scottish islands, the harsh winters and short summers, coupled with the poor-quality grazing and lack of shelter, dictated the small size of the ponies which adapted to live there. However, on the west coast of Ireland, warmed by the Gulf Stream and virtually free from frosts, the rather better grazing which was available all year round could sustain the ancestors of the Connemara ponies, which grew considerably bigger than many other types. It soon becomes apparent that the height and build of the indigenous ponies was governed by Nature or, more specifically, by climate, terrain and vegetation. Consequently, in the hypothetical situation of animals of 14 hands (142 cm) or more being turned out on Dartmoor, for example, those that survived to breed would almost certainly have reduced in height to around 12 hands (122 cm) over successive generations, eventually reaching an optimum size for the geography of the area. It is similarly likely that, if these ponies were then moved onto a remote Scottish island, their size would have reduced again over time to around 10 hands (101.6 cm) to enable them to cope with their less hospitable surroundings. Size is perhaps the most obvious way in which ponies adapt to their environment; the more subtle adaptations like coat type or changes in conformation tend to creep in almost imperceptibly over an even longer period of time. While we attribute these changes to Nature, it is almost certain that in hunting these animals for food, Man often drove the herds to the relative safety of remoter areas like the Welsh hills, thereby initiating the changes that Nature eventually wrought.

Small herds in any environment would, by this point, have also started to display family characteristics, distinguishing themselves in small ways

Terrain, climate and vegetation have been the principal influences over the centuries in determining the size of individual breeds, including the Shetland which, at maturity, must not exceed 42 inches (106.7 cm).

from other local herds, while pre-potent stallions would stamp their own identity on their progeny, thereby creating recognizable herd characteristics that would often be reinforced through inbreeding. Still a long way from being sufficiently diverse to be even in the first stages of developing into breeds, these differences were more like strains within the recognized type. Moreover, the herds were safest in those habitats where Man could not live all year round, possibly only venturing there for summer hunting, and while there may have been some movement between habitats with consequent interbreeding initially, this would have become more difficult as Man populated the lowlands and ventured into crop farming.

If the nearest comparative breed or type to the early wild pony of western Europe is the Exmoor pony of today, indisputably the purest of the British native pony breeds, the similarities go far deeper than appearance alone. Most of the characteristics of the Exmoor have changed little over thousands of years, having evolved to ensure survival in a very harsh environment. Natural selection based on survival of the fittest will have ensured that only the hardiest, most resourceful animals came through the long winters to breed in the spring. What little information we have about the aboriginal wild ponies of Britain has been collated from careful study of fossil remains unearthed at archaeological sites in the south and south-west of England where, during the Ice Age, the ice cap did not reach. Another source of reference is the cave art of France as, when most of the French cave paintings were done, the English Channel was still a marshy stretch of ground over which the pony herds roamed at will. As such, the detailed paintings in mineral pigments referred to a pony of western European type rather than an island or mainland type. The ponies were brown or greyish-dun with lighter underparts and a mealy muzzle, a colour pattern similar to both Przevalski's horse and the Tarpan. It is also a colour seen in many deer and wild cattle, suggesting that this colour pattern had become common to many herbivores grazing on open ground. The height of these early wild ponies would again have been comparable to that of the Exmoor, around 11–12 hands (112–122 cm), because the

Exmoor ponies are probably as close to the original wild pony of western Europe as any other breed in existence.

environment, especially in winter, would have dictated the size that could be maintained by the vegetation available.

A study of the European wild pony's bone structure, and the muscles it would have supported, based on archaeological evidence, seems to indicate that these ponies moved with small steps, having rather straight shoulders and a limited length of stride as a consequence, which would suit an animal living on rough ground, where sure-footedness would be essential. Generally, horses living on open, flat ground have more sloping shoulders and a longer length of stride, because flat-out speed rather than agility matters more in that terrain. The feet of the European wild pony would have been relatively small, but hard and dense for traversing rocky, broken ground without excessive wear or damage. The winter coat would have been a double coat, with an outer layer to turn the rain and an inner, denser layer to keep the animal insulated against the cold. In the late spring this would have been shed for a few short months to reveal a much finer, darker-coloured summer coat, although it is quite likely that young stock or those in poorer condition may have retained part of their long winter coat throughout the summer months. The mane and tail would have been thick, as a full and dense tail, set low on the hindquarters, would have given the pony considerable protection from driving rain or snow when the hindquarters were turned into the wind. Short, bristly hairs on the dock would have acted like a chute to throw off rain and prevent it from running down the pony's hind legs or tail, where it could have frozen in cold weather.

In addition to protection from the weather, a dense mane offered protection of another kind when stallions fought for supremacy of the little herds in the spring and would try to bite each other's necks. The head, large and rather plain to accommodate the sizeable teeth and well-developed jaw muscles, would have appeared deeper than it actually was owing to the long hair which grew under the jaw like a beard during the winter months, while the ears were small to preserve body heat lost quickly through such extremities. The nostrils would have been large to warm cold air before it entered the body cavity, and also to pick up scents more easily, since vigilance against predators could never be relaxed. Another protection against the elements was having a 'toad' eye or a raised ridge above the eye socket to channel rain away from the eyes. Because the ponies often needed a quick turn of speed to escape possible danger, this was facilitated by having a deep chest and well-sprung ribs, affording plenty of heart and lung room. The ponies lived in small family groups, which could comprise a few mares with foals and some older young stock under the supervision of a lead stallion. All members of the group remained alert and vigilant at all times, turning and galloping away at the least suspicion of danger.

EARLY DOMESTICATION AND MILITARY USE

The first accurate description we have of the native ponies of Britain comes from the writing of Julius Caesar, the Roman politician and general, who landed near Dover for the first time in 55 BC as the expanding Roman Empire reached the shores of Britain. However, the wild ponies had been domesticated by the ancient Britons long before Caesar stepped ashore at Pegwell Bay. Originally, it is highly likely that wild mares with foals at foot were trapped for use in a meat and milk husbandry system, whereby the mares were milked during lactation then killed for meat in the early winter and the foals reared for later use in haulage or transport. The wild mares could have been lamed or disabled in the trapping process, making them unsound for any work, but the hand-reared foals were a more promising prospect. Hand-rearing was a time-consuming and expensive process, as winter forage in the form of 'browse' – dried leaves, grasses and other vegetation – was difficult to collect and store in any reasonable quantity, and its nutritional content would have been low. Grain crops were grown, but the yield was not high and it is unlikely that any could have been spared for livestock when people themselves lived on meagre rations in the winter. Any fenced enclosures would have been used to keep stock safe at night from predators, especially wolves, rather than as enclosed pastures, which would have been costly in both time and materials to build and maintain. It is therefore almost certain that domesticated ponies or those captured from the wild (as the majority must have been if the British tribes used large numbers in warfare) had to graze unenclosed, perhaps under supervision and certainly restricted by tethers or hobbles.

It seems evident that, following initial domestication, the British tribes quite quickly developed the use of ponies for warfare. In the thirty-third chapter of the fourth book of his *Commentaries on the Gallic War*, Caesar wrote about the inhabitants of Britain, the chariots they used in battle and the ponies that pulled them. Bearing in mind that the Romans were poor horsemen with no equestrian traditions (preferring to use the services of mounted mercenaries when cavalry was needed for military operations rather than attempt to acquire and train their own), their comments on horse-related matters in general are always open to conjecture. However Caesar, while essentially infantry-orientated, wrote favourably of the small, wiry and nimble ponies used by the ancient Britons in harness and for pack work – although he was considerably less complimentary about their owners and Britain in general!

Caesar wrote at length about the ancient Britons' *essendum* or war chariot, which differed from the Roman chariot in being open at both the front and back rather than at the back only. It is also supposed to have had long scythes fixed to the axle trees so that, when the chariot was driven at speed through enemy lines, the effect was devastating – although no axles with scythes have yet been excavated to verify their existence. (Another Roman, Cicero, was equally impressed by these vehicles, writing to a friend that there was little to take away from Britain except the chariots.) The ancient Britons' usual method of combat was unique, as Caesar explained:

> Their mode of fighting with their chariots is this; firstly, they drive about in all directions and throw their weapons, and generally break the ranks of the enemy with the very dread of their horses and the noise of their wheels; and when they have worked themselves in between the troops of horse, leap from their chariots

and engage on foot. The charioteers meanwhile withdraw some little distance from the battle, and so place themselves with the chariots, that if their masters are overpowered by the number of the enemy they may have a ready retreat to their own troops. Thus they display in battle the speed of horse with the firmness of infantry; and by daily practice and exercise attain to such expertise, that they are accustomed, even on a declining and steep place, to check their horses at full speed, and manage and turn them in an instant, to run along the pole and stand on the yoke, and thence betake themselves with the greatest celerity to their chariots again.

While much has been written about the use of the chariot in warfare on British soil, it is evident from Caesar's recollections that the ponies were trained to an exacting standard. He actually referred to them in his *Commentaries on the Gallic War* as 'well-trained horses'. The work required regular short bursts of speed from the ponies, and these were always driven in pairs, either because their small size meant that two were actually needed to pull the load at the required speed, or because they were easier to control in pairs. As the unsprung war chariot was built with a woven floor and sides, the weight cannot have been great. Whatever the reason, the small indigenous ponies were ideal for this work, employing the stamina and speed once needed to outrun predators in the wild to sustain repeated forays into enemy lines during a battle that could last hours or even days.

An indication of the number of chariots in use by the British at the time of the Roman occupation can be deduced from what we know about the British chieftain, Cassibelaunus, who successfully took command of the previously warring tribes to oppose Caesar's second invasion of Britain in 54 BC. He had previously overthrown the king of the Trinovantes, the most powerful tribe in Britain at the time, but the king's son had fled to Gaul where Caesar was governor to seek help. When Cassibelaunus dismissed the main body of his army, he retained 'four thousand of his war chariots to harass the Roman army in their attempts to forage'. If this figure is correct, and Caesar's writings from which it is taken are generally accurate in terms of military details, the large numbers of ponies needed would imply that the wild herds from which they were drawn were extensive. Furthermore, the use of native British ponies in harness was not confined only to war chariots, for Tacitus mentions that the wives of the British charioteers watched the battles from carts positioned at the edge of the battlefield. This would seem to indicate that the wives had travelled to the battlefield in the carts, suggesting more general use of the ponies for the haulage of passengers and goods. There is, however, no evidence to suggest that ponies were selectively bred or that domesticated breeding herds were maintained.

Since it is known that the Romans had access to a great many types of horse from across the extensive Roman Empire, it is significant that Caesar was sufficiently impressed by the ponies of Britain to take a number of them back to Rome. However, it is unlikely that these ponies had a military purpose, as most Roman cavalry took the form of foreign mercenaries, who were required to provide their own weapons and mounts. Despite commonly held but erroneous beliefs, the chariot horse of the Roman hippodromes and arenas was little bigger than the British pony and some of these British ponies may well have ended up on the racetracks that provided popular entertainment for the masses. However, some centuries later, St. Augustine provided a clue to another possible use when he wrote: 'The *mannii*, or ponies that were brought from Britain, are those chiefly in use by jugglers and strollers, to exhibit the feats of their craft.' Apparently, their owners also fancifully shaved or clipped the upper part of the ponies' shaggy bodies to give them a more singular appearance.

Up until the time when horses were imported into Britain during the Roman occupation as mercenary cavalry mounts, it would seem evident that, notwithstanding some regional variation, the pony population of Britain would still have been sufficiently consistent in overall appearance to be recognizable as one *type*. There is evidence to support the belief that this uniform national type survived to some extent even up until the nineteenth century when semi-feral or even wild herds ran freely in many of the remoter parts of Britain. Lord Arthur Cecil, a founder member of the Riding and

Polo Pony Society (eventually to become the National Pony Society), was one individual who had noticed the striking similarities between all the British native pony breeds. Writing in 1899 about pony breeds in general he noted: 'There are many characteristics which all these possess in common, notably the clean-cut head, small ears, bright full eye and well-curved nostrils together with a strong predisposition to the brown colour with light tan or mealy points, which we see running through as a common attribute of them all.' Five years later he added the comment that: 'New Forest ponies had shown characteristics of the original British pony until the early 1800s.' When he tried the experiment of bringing ten Exmoors into the forest in 1910, he noted: 'Everyone of the old commoners were unanimous (not knowing them to be Exmoors) in saying, "Ah, that was the old kind of pony which lived in the forest".' Thomas Dykes, writing in 1905 of the extinct Staffa pony of the Scottish islands, said they were 'the true brown with mealy nose and belly so often seen in native ponies of all breeds'. He went on to add that the ponies of a neighbouring island, Barra, were a similar colour. Early photographs of other breeds often show a similar trend, including one of North Wales ponies taken in 1901 which shows a number of ponies with the characteristic lighter muzzle and underbelly of their wild ancestors. The photograph of an 'unimproved Welsh Mountain pony' in Captain Hayes' book, *Points of a Horse*, published in 1904, also shows an animal closely fitting the stamp of native wild pony at the time of the Roman invasion in size, build and colour. This evidence is further supported by a statement made by General Pitt Rivers, an archaeologist excavating around Cranborne Chase in the late nineteenth century, who believed that: 'The Exmoor pony is probably the nearest approach that can be found at the present time to the horse of the Romanized Britons in this district'. Fell pony breeders of the twentieth century could recall that the ponies of their youth were much smaller than they are today, often no more than 13 hands (132 cm), rather lighter in build, with tremendous stamina and usually brown in colour – and Dartmoor ponies with a lighter-coloured muzzle were also not uncommon at that time.

The author's great uncle on his Welsh pony, circa 1890. Brown or dun with a paler muzzle, and sometimes a lighter underbelly, were common colours in all native pony breeds at one time.

An Exmoor pony showing the original coat and muzzle pattern which is still a characteristic of this breed.

When all these points are viewed in comparison, an image emerges of a distinct and consistent stamp of pony and this leads us to speculate that, in the remoter parts of the British Isles and away from Man's attempts to improve on Nature through selective breeding and the introduction of external blood, something akin to the wild British pony somehow managed to survive until comparatively recent times. Even with the diversity of British pony breeds we have today, it is likely that the blood of the original British pony is not too far beneath the surface, rather as the Tarpan was with the Konik pony of Poland. The question has to be asked: 'Why did the British pony not then survive as one fairly standard national breed, with some regional variations, and why do the British Isles have more distinct native breeds, both horse and pony, than any other part of the world?

Chapter 2

EARLY TRADERS
AND INVADERS

A horse is a vain thing for safety.
PSALM 23, VERSE 17

It is highly probable that without Man's intervention, or more precisely the importation of outside blood and the process of selective breeding to produce definite types of equines for specific purposes, there would now be few pony breeds and no horse breeds at all in Britain.

Two factors governed the importation of foreign horses; a sound and logical reason for doing so, and the means of transporting a large and strong animal by sea. Although sea-going vessels able to carry men, arms, goods and small livestock existed earlier, it was not until the period later called the Iron Age (800 BC up until the time of the Roman invasion), that there were ships large enough and strong enough to carry horses, and even then it would have been necessary for the horses to have been hobbled or incapacitated in some way. During the Iron Age, the population of Britain had increased substantially and was probably in excess of a million, this growth being partly attributable to improved crop yields, particularly barley and wheat although peas, beans and flax (which provided edible linseed) were also grown. Farming techniques also improved and the introduction of iron ploughshares made it possible to cultivate larger areas of fertile, heavy clay soils. Increased productivity gave scope for trading, and archaeologists have confirmed by their discovery at burial sites in Britain of artefacts from other parts of Europe that trading and exchange contracts between Britain, mainland Europe and also further afield had developed long before the Bronze Age (approx. 1700–800 BC) and had continued over the centuries. The discovery of some blue glass beads in Wiltshire, identical to those found at Deir el-Bahari and dating back to around 1400 BC indicates trade routes between Britain and Egypt, and opens up the question of whether horses could have been imported into Britain before the Romans stepped ashore here.

EARLY CELTIC INFLUENCES

Some historians believe that Celtic traders may have been the first to come to Britain to exchange pottery, weapons, jewellery (including the blue glass Egyptian beads) and horses for tin and copper. The loose grouping of tribes we now call the Celts originated around central Europe and spread out across the whole of Europe, up into Scandinavia and down into the Iberian Peninsula, their culture dominating those of the peoples they encountered. They were horsemen and riders (a chronicler of the time recorded that the Celts in battle would cut off the heads of their fallen enemies and hang them from their horses' necks), which probably indicates that their mounts may have been somewhat larger than the early native ponies of Britain. The importance of the horse to the Celts is indicated by their practice of burying a chieftain with his war chariot and horses for use in the afterlife. Given the wide trading network they had established, it is not unreasonable to speculate that the best of their horses contained at least a splash of eastern blood.

There is evidence of Celtic settlers in Ireland around 500 BC, although it is unclear at what point they became the dominant Irish ethnic group, having spread west across Ireland over a period of several hundred years. However, it is known that, about a century before Julius Caesar's assault on Britain, a tribe of Celts known as the Belgae settled in what is now the East Riding of Yorkshire, bringing horses with them, and when Caesar defeated the three Celtic tribes of Gaul (now mainly modern France) in 56 BC, many of the defeated Celts fled to Britain, taking their possessions, including horses, with them. Another Celtic tribe, the Veneti, from what is now Brittany, were skilled sailors, shipwrights and traders, and supplied ships to ferry the escaping refugees across the Channel and into southern England.

THE PHOENICIAN THEORY

However, the Celts may not have been the only horse-owning immigrants before the arrival of the Romans. Julius Caesar was of the opinion that the Phoenicians preceded the Roman invasion of Britain in 55 BC by some years. The Phoenicians' home was the strip of land we know today as Palestine, Israel, Lebanon and the coastal part of Syria and, unlike most ancient peoples, they did not rely primarily on agriculture. Instead, from the beginnings of their known history (some time after 2900 BC), they were sailors, skilled navigators and traders. Their land was fertile but limited in size and they probably developed their skills as boat-builders (learnt from their neighbours, particularly the Egyptians) initially to be able to fish the rich Mediterranean to support their expanding population. The availability of large quantities of home-grown cedar wood, which they also shipped and sold to neighbouring countries, gave them the raw materials to build up a considerable fleet of ships. In addition to their seafaring exploits, the Phoenicians turned their cities into great centres of manufacturing where they produced jewellery, furniture and cloth, and to produce these goods for export they needed the raw materials. Their early trading activities grew into a culture based on commerce and colonization, and by 1500 BC they had built a chain of ports with natural harbours along the coastline they occupied, and went on to establish trading ports on the present-day sites of Marseilles in southern France and Cadiz in Spain, in Tunisia, Malta, down the west coast of Africa and (c. 814 BC) in Carthage on the coast of North Africa. The Phoenicians traded goods including timber, ivory, gold, silver, silks, spices, precious stones, glassware, cotton and linen cloth between all these sites. They also, significantly, traded horses – for which they found a growing market in the lands bordering the Mediterranean, including North Africa.

The Phoenicians were known to have had two types of ships: 'long' ships used for warfare and designed for speed, with two banks of oars and a central mast from which a sail could be raised to supplement the energies of the oarsmen, and 'round' ships for trade which were smaller and had no sails, relying on oarsmen solely to power them. An Assyrian wall relief from the city of Nineveh, recounting the flight of the Phoenician king from the port of Tyre in 710 BC, clearly shows both types of ship. The prows of these ships were often depicted in the art of the time as having carved horses' heads of Arab type, perhaps signifying their most revered cargo. It is known that the Persians had developed special ships for the transportation of war horses; King Darius used such ships to move his cavalry by sea in 490 BC when he attacked Greece with his horsemen. The Phoenician trading ships could similarly have carried horses and, with military supremacy in the ancient world growing increasingly dependent on horsepower, these enterprising traders would have been quick to exploit a growing market. While the carrying capacity of the individual Phoenician ships was limited, their deployment in trading activities was extensive and, for safety reasons, they often travelled in small fleets. An Egyptian narrative of around 1,080 BC tells the story of one Phoenician merchant living at Tanis on the Nile delta who had as many as fifty cargo ships plying back and forth between the port of Sidon and the Nile.

In the Royal Exchange in London is a painting by Lord Leighton showing Phoenician merchants visiting Britain, but there has always been some controversy among historians as to whether they ever came to Britain or not, despite Julius Caesar's claims. The journey from Carthage (from where the ships would have set sail) although difficult, was not beyond their capabilities, and many historians believe they did come to Britain, sailing around Spain to Cornwall where, either from initial exploration or through information supplied by other early traders, they knew there was copper and tin available – if they could persuade the locals to part with it. It is quite possible that they went to Ireland, too. At the time of the English invasion of Ireland in AD 1172, the invaders were surprised to find the Irish riding with no saddles or bridles, using only a simple halter with a lead-rope and a stick with a crook at the end. Giraldus Cambrensis said of them: 'They drive on and guide their horses by means of a stick with a crook at the upper end which they hold in their hand.' These sticks were curiously similar to the sticks used by Arabs, the crook end being used to catch the nose-rings of camels, and many believe them to have been introduced into Ireland by the Phoenicians. Centuries earlier, Plutarch had written of Julius Caesar riding without a bridle, and Geoffrey Gambada, riding instructor to the Doge of Venice, writing in 1787, alluded to this when he wrote: 'How Julius Caesar stopped his horse, when he rode with his hands behind him, I am at a loss to divine.' It can be deduced that this unusual style of horsemanship, derived from the Numidians in what is now Algeria, was not uncommon in Caesar's time and styles of riding were often imported along with the horses of the exporting culture. In the sixteenth century, Spencer wrote of women in Ireland riding side-saddle on the off-side of the horse, a Spanish and Northern African custom possibly picked up from Iberian traders since, in the rest of Europe, most women riding side-saddle rode on the near-side.

If the Phoenicians did bring horses to Britain, they must have carried considerable trading kudos. Horses were expensive to buy, and were not the easiest cargo to load and unload without risk of injury and loss of value, bearing in mind the lack of ports in Britain at the time and the fact that horses had to be winched overboard and down into the sea and were then expected to swim ashore with the guidance of a groom. They were also a vulnerable cargo, particularly on long journeys. Horses would have drunk a lot of water, especially on a sea journey because of the salt air and the dry rations they were expected to survive on, and fresh water, like the feedstuffs for the horses, was a bulky cargo taking up precious storage space. Losses during a rough crossing could deplete profits. The horses therefore had to carry a high price and that meant they had to be something exceptional. If the only equines in Britain at the time were ponies of around 12 hands (122 cm), a much larger horse of eastern blood would have had a rarity value and commanded a correspondingly high price in trade negotiations. Such horses, like the white 'high horse' ridden by Queen Elizabeth I when she went among her subjects in later times, were ideal for chieftains, raising them above their troops both literally and psychologically.

The Phoenicians bought the horses they traded from Syria and also from Cappodocia, an extensive district of Asia Minor, now modern Turkey but, in the sixth century BC, part of the vast Persian Empire. The Cappadocians had got their first horses and learnt the basic skills of horsemanship from the Scythians of southern Russia, whose foundation stock was of Mongolian pony descent and described by J. K. Anderson, an American authority on the horses of ancient times, as: 'Useful, strong ponies, with coarse necks and shoulders, very low withers and coarse heads.' However, the Scythians were great traders and horse-breeders and quickly improved the quality of their extensive herds by acquiring stock from other sources. Evidence of this comes from the horses buried in their tombs in the Altai Mountains, which date back to 450 BC: these include animals of Ferghana type, a prized strain from Turkestan standing up to 15 hands (152.5 cm). By successful cross-breeding with other strains of horses, hybrid vigour was introduced into the Scythian herds, contributing towards the increased height and general stature of individual animals. The Scythian horses were renowned for their beauty, speed and stamina, and it is said that Philip of Macedonia, father of Alexander the Great, seized 20,000 Scythian mares to boost the quality of his herds.

Scythian horses were sold to the Assyrians, Hykos, Parthians and Cappadocians, who also acquired horses from Syria where vast herds were maintained. In the third century BC a Syrian ruler called Seleucis Nicator maintained a royal stud of 30,000 mares and 300 stallions, and huge breeding herds were also kept in many neighbouring countries. Herodotus wrote of a provincial governor in Assyria who reputedly had 16,000 mares and 800 stallions, while a letter from the Hittite King to the King of Babylon, circa 1275 BC, commented that there were 'more horses than stalks of straw'. In Cappadocia itself in the second millennium BC the herds were said to be so large that they could not be corralled or contained in any way. Considering that the mortality rate for cavalry horses was very high, it was only because the herds from which such animals were drawn were so large that the use of cavalry in warfare was able to expand so rapidly. The Greeks called the Cappadocians 'Syrians' or 'White Syrians', but the name Cappadocia came from the Persian word *Katpatuka* meaning 'the land of beautiful horses' – evidence of the esteem in which Cappodocian horses were held, and the reason why they were of such interest to the Phoenician traders. According to Youatt: 'In the fourth century AD the Roman Emperor sent two hundred Cappadocian horses as the most acceptable gift he could offer to a powerful prince of Arabia.'

It can be assumed that many of the horses the Phoenicians brought from Syria or Cappodocia were of Arab type, although as no recognized breeds existed at that time and names were used loosely to describe countries of origin rather than parentage, it is difficult to be precise. There are strong arguments to say that the Arab breed did not originate on the Arabian Peninsula but with the people of Persia (modern day Iran), Iraq, Syria and Turkey, who were referred to as Arabs before the present-day country of Saudi Arabia even existed. There is evidence that the domesticated horse was introduced into Asia Minor, northern Syria and Mesopotamia around 2500 BC by invaders or migrants from further north, although others believe that the ancestors of the Arab were wild horses from northern Syria, southern Turkey and possibly further east, as this area offered a climate with enough rain and sufficiently mild temperatures to provide a perfect environment for horse breeding. The first breeding stock in the Arabian Peninsula was not obtained until during the sixth century AD following raids on Persia where the so-called Persian Arab, described as 'one of the earliest known domesticated breeds of horse' had existed since around 2000 BC and was esteemed throughout the ancient world. Herodotus described these horses as 'fast, spirited, beautiful and imbued with sufficient stamina to enable them to gallop for up to thirty miles'. So integral to Persian culture were their horses that a law was passed prohibiting horse owners from walking!

Selective breeding over a long period produced the Arab as we know it today, but it is probable that the 'eastern' horses traded by the Phoenicians were quality animals standing 14–15 hands (142–152.5 cm), which was considered large at the time, being fleet of foot and refined. If such horses did reach Britain then, in comparison to the wiry native ponies of Britain, they must have looked quite exceptional.

Another early type of horse known and accessible to the Phoenician traders was the Barb horse, which hailed from the region nowadays comprising the countries of Morocco, Tunisia, Algeria and Libya. Although often assumed to be an offshoot of the Arab, the Barb bore little physical resemblance to that breed – although sharing other qualities like great stamina and powers of endurance. The Barb was, and still is to this day, a type more than a breed, furthermore displaying considerable variation in type, partly as a result of cross-breeding with the Arab but also owing to regional differences along the North African coastline. Its fame lay in its physical capabilities rather than its looks, for the Barb is distinguished by its rather large head, often with a pronounced convex profile, which it tends to pass on along with its more favourable qualities to its descendants.

THE ROMANS

Even if equine imports into Britain can be attributed to the Phoenicians, there are no clear indications that they had any real impact on the native stock of the British Isles, but when it comes to the Romans, the evidence for their imports and the impact they had is well documented. When the expansion of the Roman Empire brought the first Romans to Britain in 55 BC, the Roman troops were pinned down on a beach-head for two months and, with the approaching autumn gales, they withdrew to return the following year. Caesar had horses with him when he first landed for he recorded in his *Commentaries on the Gallic War* that the cavalry (in reality Gallic auxiliaries under their own chieftain) were seasick and he sent them back to Gaul. After a number of subsequent landings and sporadic warfare with the local tribes they encountered, the Romans settled in various parts of Britain on a permanent basis from the middle of the first century AD and set up military bases and trading centres. The Romans' military supremacy was always at threat from the local tribes under their respective chieftains and it was to augment their armed forces that they followed a pattern which had worked successfully for them in other parts of the Empire and recruited mercenaries from other countries. These were employed for an agreed contracted period, and they were paid directly by the army paymaster. In AD 176, a contingent of Sarmatian horsemen (the tribe who had driven the Scythians from their homeland and taken control of some of the breeding herds of horses), were recruited to serve in Britain alongside ousted Scythian warriors. Other mercenaries in the employment of Rome included foreign units from Hungary, Poland, North Africa, France, Belgium, Friesland and northern Spain. Like most mercenaries, they were required to provide their own weapons but, more significantly, cavalry regiments had to provide their own mounts. These troops travelled overland from their countries of origin and were transported across the English Channel either in Roman craft, which were large enough to carry horses, or more probably in the boats of coastal-living subjects like the Celtic Veneti from France.

By the end of the second century AD there were twenty-eight cavalry units of mercenaries in Britain, and the majority would have been mounted on horses they had brought with them. With losses arising from death and serious injury in warfare, it was estimated that a cavalry regiment needed around 500 horses at its disposal if it was to maintain its effectiveness as a fighting unit. Therefore, while it might originally have been the case that mercenaries from a certain area would all be mounted on horses from that region (Hungarian mercenaries all mounted on Hungarian horses, for example), it is unlikely that this status quo would have remained for long. In addition to replacing lost, lame, injured or unsuitable horses, mercenaries regularly sold or traded them so, on a long campaign or journey, a succession of mounts derived from different areas would be quite feasible. Despite this, some horses indigenous to the countries their owners came from would have made it to Britain. The Scythians and Sarmatians would have set out on their journeys on a similar stamp of horse to those possibly imported earlier by the Phoenicians. As for the Spanish mercenaries, it is known that the Romans transported large numbers of Numidian horses into the Iberian Peninsula, which became the premier centre in the Empire for the production of top-quality horses. Their Numidian horses' forebears had been introduced into North Africa by the Hykos (whose name literally translates as 'ruler of foreign lands'), who seized power in lower Egypt in the seventeenth century BC. The Hykos has obtained at least some of their original horses from the Scythians, so the links are many. North African horses were renowned for their quiet temperaments and Strabo described them as 'small, obedient and swift', exploding the myth that all North African horses were large in size.

Early Roman writers divided all horses into three groups according to their purpose. Vegetius wrote:

> For war, the Huns, Thuringian, Burgundian and Friesian horse excel; next those of Epirus, Sarmatia and Dalmatia; for chariots, the Cappadocian. In the circus the Spanish horse excels all others, and also the Sicilian, although the African horses of Spanish blood are the swiftest of any. For the saddle above all the Persian horses, being the easiest in their carriage and most soft in their step.

Clearly, the Romans and their supporting troops had access to a great many types of horse from across the Roman Empire and, from archaeological evidence, we know that many were brought to Britain. In addition, some of the mercenaries were mounted on ponies, and others brought horses of the type the Romans deemed best suited to warfare – that is, large horses of considerable substance whose ancestors were the Forest horses of earlier times. In Roman times, horses with Forest-type ancestry, coarse-boned animals with large heads, were bred in many parts of the Empire and used for both draught work and riding. The Germanic tribes were said to be mounted on such animals, which Tacitus described as 'slow, heavy and powerful'. The best of this stamp of horse came from Friesland, a province of some importance in Roman times, now roughly divided between Holland and Germany. The fertile, sandy lowlands produced an animal that would become one of the oldest recognizable breeds in Europe. The Friesian, a substantially-built but active horse of up to 15 hands (152.5 cm), was usually black in colour with few or no white markings, and was renowned for its strength and stamina and also for an action that was both elevated and ground-covering. Furthermore, it was noted for its docile and willing temperament, enabling unskilled men to handle it, and it attracted the interest of the Romans, who saw it as an ideal draught animal.

Like so many coastal dwellers, the Friesian people were great seafarers and traders and their deep-bodied, broad and capacious merchant ships were capable of carrying all manner of cargo, including horses. They traded in a variety of goods including cloth, swords, metalwork and horses and, like their Celtic contemporaries, they could have visited British shores before the Romans. Place names like Friston in Suffolk certainly testify to the extent of their later travel and, at one time, there was a Friesian trading post in the city of York, while Dumfries in southern Scotland literally means 'hill of the Friesians'. As well as being traders in their own right, the Friesian seafarers were more than prepared to hire out their boats and labour for the transport of goods and personnel, and it is quite probable that the Friesians played a vital role in the Roman invasion of Britain by ferrying soldiers, arms, equipment and horses across the Channel.

In AD120 the Emperor Hadrian decreed that a wall should be built right across the north of Britain from the Solway to the mouth of the Tyne, a distance of 73 miles (117 km), which would control the movement of people and separate what is now England and Wales, which were under Roman rule, from Scotland and the war-like Picts, who made repeated raids on Roman settlements. Apart from occasional forays into Scotland and trade with Ireland, the lands beyond Hadrian's Wall were largely unaffected by Roman rule. Built to a height of 15 ft (4.5 m) and constructed of stone (except for the western section which was made of blocks of turf), the wall was a potent symbol of Roman rule.

Although, when finished, the wall was patrolled by large numbers of mercenaries, it was actually built by Roman troops rather than conscripted labour (with 10,000 soldiers assigned to the task), and a considerable amount of horsepower was needed for the haulage work necessary with such a major construction project. This haulage work was undertaken either by pack animals or by pulling the blocks of stone used to build the wall over rollers, in the same way as the ancient Egyptians had moved the stone for the pyramids. The native ponies of the region were too small for this work but the larger and heavier horses of Friesland and Germany were ideal and, in addition to those brought over as the personal property of mercenaries, the Romans imported substantial numbers of these active draught horses.

In Roman society, where it was considered decadent to ride in a horse-drawn vehicle rather than on a horse, officers would often ride at the head of their infantry, their elevated position denoting their rank and making them visible to their troops. For this role, a horse of some size and quality was required and these animals, widely assumed to be Arabs, had to be imported into Britain. According to traditional belief, Julius Caesar was so impressed by the ponies running wild on the Gower peninsular in Wales that he set up a stud at Bala in Merionethshire to improve the native ponies by using Arab blood. Although the Arab is a breed of great antiquity, the term 'Arab' has often been used indiscriminately to mean any horse of eastern blood, but the bones of horses with all the characteristics of Arabs have been excavated at military sites where one might expect officers' horses to have been stabled. Horse racing was also introduced into Britain by the Romans and their Syrian legions, and by the fourth century AD there were hippodromes at Dorchester, Silchester, Banbury, St. Albans and other venues where horses of primarily eastern blood raced, implying that there were many horses of this type in Britain by at that time.

Most of the horses of whatever type imported into Britain would have been stallions, for it was customary not to ride or drive mares, partly because the herd system for keeping horses meant that mares would constantly be in-foal or have a foal or yearling at foot, and also because the tradition for riding stallions only was well established in most cultures, including the Romans'. It was also believed that gelding a horse reduced its strength, although some of the mercenaries, notably the Scythians, were skilled in the practice of castration and rode only geldings, despite Pliny the Elder's erroneous statement that they preferred to ride mares.

Hard evidence of the types of horse in Britain at the time of the Roman occupation can be found in both fossilized remains and in art. The latter is open to speculation, for depictions of horses in stone carvings, on coins and jewellery are usually meant to be decorative rather than factual, and often a person of importance and their mount are depicted larger than their peers as testimony to their place in society, making it difficult to assess the size or type of horses. Thus, artistic representation could be a long way from actual reality. For example, in trying to form a picture of early Scythian horses, we find that the only depictions in their art are stylized completely. However, a study of horses' bones excavated from the sites of Roman settlements and forts gives a more accurate picture. One site, Newstead in Roxburghshire, produced a wealth of bones from which the following could be identified:

- A small pony not exceeding 11 hands (112 cm) and recognizable as a Shetland pony type, proof that the Island type of pony was established at this time.
- A slightly larger pony of up to 12 hands (122 cm) which would correspond to the mainland indigenous type of pony.

- A still larger pony, with slender bones, which could have been an import.
- An Arab type standing about 14 hands (142 cm) which would certainly not have been indigenous.
- Two heavier-built and coarser animals, one standing up to 15 hands (152.5 cm), again imported and undoubtedly of Forest type, possibly an import from Friesland.

By the end of the third century AD, the Roman occupation of Britain was in a state of demise, partly because the legions were being repeatedly recalled to Rome to defend their besieged city (or some other part of the Empire) from enemy attack, and partly because the infrastructure of the Roman military system was crumbling as a result of power struggles between commanders, corruption, and military orders not being communicated, which resulted in confusion and supplies not reaching outlying stations. The mercenaries, whose motive in fighting for the Romans was purely financial, began taking what money they could get and returning home, generally leaving their horses behind as, aside from the cost and risks of transporting them back across the Channel, they commanded a higher price in Britain than they would back home in mainland Europe. (Although the Romans never made military ventures into Ireland, it is not improbable that there were Irish mercenaries in their employ and that, as the Empire crumbled into disarray, they returned home, possibly taking horses with them in lieu of the pay that never turned up). A few mercenaries did, however, stay on. Proof that some of the Friesian mercenaries made their home in Britain comes from place-names like Frizington in Cumbria which, roughly translated from the Anglo-Saxon means 'village of the sons of the Friesians'.

By the fourth century AD, the mercenaries in the employ of the Romans had been replaced by federates, another kind of mercenary not so closely integrated into the Roman military system. The federates were more like small private armies headed by their own chieftains who, at the end of a campaign, were given a lump sum by the army paymaster which they distributed among their men as they thought fit. There is evidence of Friesian men employed as mercenaries by the Romans, and a cohort of Friesian mercenaries, around 600 men with at least some of their own horses, was stationed at the fort of Rudchester on Hadrian's Wall at one stage. There were other Friesian squadrons on the wall, and one of these independent squadrons of Friesian cavalry, known as Prince Hnaufrid's Own, was stationed in the central section of the wall. Another mounted unit, the Cuneus Frisonum Aballavenis, was stationed at Burgh by Sands near the west coast, or at Papcastle, near Cockermouth. Elsewhere in the country, federates from Spain – the principal horse-breeding region of the Roman Empire – worked alongside mercenaries from almost every corner of the Empire, some being second, third or fourth generation and by this time at least partially integrated into British society and culture.

By the end of the Roman occupation, the regional variations within the native pony population of the British Isles would have been a little more distinct, as increasing cultivation of the land and grazing of common ground by domesticated livestock would have further isolated the wild herds. Imported horses of heavier draught type from the Low Countries, as well as horses of Arab blood from eastern Europe, were also now present and, although some of the latter may not have survived the climate, it is likely that some of the progeny of those that did would have been absorbed into the local herds, losing size over successive generations.

Throughout the period of Roman rule, the Picts, who hailed from what is now Scotland, had made repeated attacks on Roman fortifications and outposts and, as mentioned earlier, Hadrian's Wall was constructed in part to control their movements and safeguard settlements from attack. The Picts were essentially cattle thieves, but they were not averse to taking other stock, harvested crops or anything else which may have been of value to them, including horses. Their raiding parties could be either relatively small affairs, involving only a handful of men and taking just two or three days, or they could be large-scale projects employing large numbers of men and taking many months. Neither were these raids restricted to the north of

England, for there is evidence of raiding parties as far south as Suffolk. With the Romans gone, their raids became both more numerous and more extensive in geographical terms. To travel large distances, horses were a necessity and the Picts had access to several different types within their home territory, from the Scottish Island type of small pony, characterized by the Shetland, to the larger lowland animals from which the Highland pony developed. In addition, they increased their extensive herds with stolen horses, including imported animals from Roman stables, and animals they traded or acquired on their widespread travels (during which times they distributed many regional types to other areas).

Although Britain had none of the cave art of western Europe, the Picts were the first inhabitants of these islands to leave any artistic representations of their horses. Their unique art, which was often highly realistic and detailed, was expressed in the durable medium of stone carving. It is on the crosses, slabs and pillars (often referred to as Pictish symbol stones), and on the memorial stones of kings and chieftains, depicting the deceased's life in lavishly decorated scenes of hunting and warfare, that we see illustrations of the horses of the time. There were recognizable Shetland pony types, larger animals assumed by comparison to human figures and illustrations of other animals to be up to 14 hands (142 cm), some quite plain sorts showing a predominance of Forest blood, and some quality animals.

On the tombstone of a Pictish princess from Cadboll in Caithness is the depiction of a horse pacing rather than trotting, which might indicate that it was not a native pony but perhaps an import stolen in a raid. Another possible explanation is that the Celtic invaders had brought small horses with them from Spain, which they distributed in several parts of the British Isles, including Ireland. These Asturian ponies were small, rarely over 11–12 hands (112–122 cm), but hardy and tough, for they hailed from the mountainous area of their homeland. They were well-known to the Romans, who used them extensively, and Pliny (AD 23–79) described them as 'a small breed that did not trot, but moved in an easy gait by alternately moving both legs on one side'. The Romans' knowledge of laterally gaited horses was supported by Secundus, who also wrote of Spanish horses which 'have not the usual gaits in running – but a smooth pace, straightening the near and off-side legs alternately, from which the horses are taught by training to adopt an ambling pace'. We know that foreign mercenaries contracted to the Romans and working in Britain had laterally gaited horses because Tacitus, writing about first-century mercenaries from Germanic tribes, said they taught their horses to pace by tying the legs together on one side. (The Persians also taught horses to pace using special hobbles, as a pacer was more comfortable to ride over a long distance than a horse that trotted). Whatever these horses' precise method of arrival, the Pictish carvings seem to indicate that some of them ended up in northern Scotland.

THE ANGLO-SAXONS

With the final withdrawal of the Roman legions from British soil around AD 408, a new wave of horse-owning immigrants, principally the Angles, Saxons and Jutes, began settling in Britain during the fifth and sixth centuries. Known collectively as the Anglo-Saxons, they either rowed themselves across the North Sea in wooden ships or used the more spacious craft of the coastal inhabitants to ferry them and their possessions over, just as the Romans had done. Their homeland was Germania, which really meant those parts of northern Europe settled by barbarian Germanic tribes, namely the coastline of mainland Europe from Denmark down the present-day coastlines of modern Germany, the Netherlands and France. The eighth-century Northumbrian monk, Bede, wrote in his *Ecclesiastical History of the English People* in 731 that the invaders:

> …came from three most powerful Germanic tribes, the Saxons, the Angles, and the Jutes. Of Jutish origin are the people of Kent and of the Isle of Wight, and the part of the kingdom of Wessex opposite the Isle of Wight, still called the nation of the Jutes. From the Saxon land, that is from the place which is now called Old

Saxony, came the East Saxons, the South Saxons, and the West Saxons. From the Anglian land, that is the place between the realm of the Jutes and the Saxons which is called *Angulus,* and remains deserted to this day, came the East Angles, the Middle Angles, the Mercians, and the Northumbrian peoples, that is, those who dwell north of the river Humber, as well as other Anglian peoples.

(Bede also gives us an insight to the ecclesiastical attitude towards horses and riding during the eighth century. He tells us that prelates and other churchmen generally travelled on foot 'but if on urgent occasions they were obliged to ride, they used mares only'. Writing centuries later, Berenger, Gentleman of the Horse to George III, was probably correct in suggesting that this was 'as a mark of humility, the mare not being so full of pride and spirit as the horse'.)

There is evidence that raiding parties from the invading tribes first came to Britain some time before they began any major settlement, for the Roman historian, Ammianus Marcellinus, records there being *Saxones* among the barbarians (mainly Picts and Irish, the latter sometimes confusingly called Scots) who were harassing the Britons in around AD 365. By around AD 450 the tribes were well established and had driven the Britons further west into Cornwall, Wales, and the west coast of Scotland. The Saxons established kingdoms in Wessex, Sussex, Middlesex and Essex, while the Angles were in control of the northern and also the eastern areas of England, the latter becoming known as East Anglia. The Jutes occupied Kent, the Isle of Wight and Hampshire, with large numbers of Jutes living in the New Forest which, until the eleventh century, was known as *Ytene* meaning 'of the Jutes'.

The Angles were probably the main force behind the wave of invasion and it is from the south-eastern area of Britain where they settled, known as Anglesland, that we get the name England. Although some historians have questioned the extent to which the Anglo-Saxons used horses, or even if they brought any with them to Britain, part of the wealth of these tribes lay in horses. Also, while these invaders would have been aware of the availability of horses in Britain, some of which would have been seized in raids, they would have needed at least a pool of horses initially in order to carry out the raids, and long-distance travel would not have been undertaken without adequate supplies of horses. That they undertook long journeys in large bands is evidenced by the fact that, in AD 685, they marched into Scotland, where they were defeated by the huge Pictish army at the battle of Dunnichen. After any battles of such scale, there were always loose horses to be gathered up by the victors or local people, one factor which would have added to the wider distribution of various types.

THE VIKINGS

In the summer of AD 793, Norwegian pirates from the Hardanger region first landed on the shores of Britain and ransacked Holy Island off the coast of Northumberland, returning the following year to plunder a monastery at the mouth of the River Wear. The results, for them, must have been disappointing, for the fabled treasures of the holy place consisted mainly of books and the Northmen or 'Norsemen' as they were called could not read. Undaunted, over the next 270 years the Scandinavian pirates (their alternative name, 'Viking', meaning 'pirate raiders') from the present-day countries of Norway, Denmark and Sweden, undertook pillaging forays which increased in both number and extent until most of the British coastline had experienced their attacks, and Viking chieftains ruled much of England, the north and west of Scotland (including all the Scottish islands), the Isle of Man, North Wales, Anglesey and parts of Ireland. The rest of northern and eastern England that was in Danish hands was known as Danelaw, as evidenced by place names with Scandinavian origins that end in -thorpe, -toft, -by or -thwaite.

Although pirating was a major pursuit for the Vikings, it was in fact a seasonal one, since they were also farmers, growing oatmeal and rye from which they made bread, and barley from which they brewed beer. Between the spring planting and the autumn harvesting was the time for raiding and, owing to the northerly latitude of their homeland, there were often late spring frosts which meant that ploughing, harrowing and sowing had to be done swiftly. For this reason, the Vikings used horses for ploughing when most other cultures, including the British, used oxen, which were considerably slower. For this work as well as for warfare, the Norsemen used the native Scandinavian ponies which stood a little over 12 hands (122 cm) and were the progenitors of the present-day Norwegian Fjord pony. Early carvings on monumental stones indicate that these were quite stocky animals, and they were usually (but not always) the dun colour with eel-stripe and zebra markings of their Steppe ancestors. Surplus colts were gelded, which initiated the first steps of selective breeding while making available for everyday work a supply of geldings, which promoted more widespread use of horsepower for a variety of purposes. When the Vikings began settling in Britain (probably because the land and climate were better suited than their homelands for agriculture), they brought many of their practices with them, including gelding, and the use of horses for ploughing and pulling sledges to transport harvested crops. In time, these practices were copied by the indigenous British, leading to the wider use of horsepower in general in Britain.

Many historians believe that, in addition to bringing their equestrian practices with them, the Vikings, like other invaders before them, also brought horses. The Vikings boats were built to a number of different designs according to use and they could certainly have carried horses, but the Vikings would not have taken horses to Britain unless they were intending to stay there with some degree of permanence and unless they considered that the local ponies were, in their eyes, inferior to the Scandinavian animals. If we consider that they visited coastal areas first and may, initially, have encountered the small ponies of the Scottish islands, this could have been a reason for bringing their own stock. It may not be insignificant that the dun colour, usually with a dark eel-stripe and sometimes zebra markings down the legs, is found most commonly in those native breeds in parts of Britain once colonized by Vikings, that is to say the Highland pony of Scotland, the Connemara pony of Ireland, and some of the ponies of Wales.

The Vikings may also have introduced Norwegian ponies and the heavier 'Forest' type of Danish horses into Britain for a reason totally unconnected with agriculture – the sport of stallion fighting – although its popularity was relatively short-lived and it was soon discontinued as the invaders gradually converted to Christianity. The Church outlawed the sport because of its connections with pagan fertility cults and because the stallions could only be induced to fight by the presence of an in-season mare. The losing stallion was generally killed (if not already dead) and then eaten as part of a wider event involving heavy drinking and licentious behaviour. The association between eating horse flesh and paganism was to endure for centuries as a consequence of the abhorrence of the Christian Church. However, during the period when stallion fighting was still prevalent, it might be surmised that the Vikings brought their Norwegian stallions over to Britain to match them against the small indigenous ponies, as the imported animals were of stronger build and therefore more likely to succeed.

As stallion fighting waned in popularity, the sport of racing took its place, but this was not galloping but trotting, and the Norse word for the sport was *hestakeith*, which is derived from the old Norse verb *skeitha*, meaning to pace. The sites of these trotting races were widespread, as indicated by associated place names, ranging from Hesketh Grange in North Yorkshire to Wickham Skeith in Suffolk and Hesket New Market in Cumbria. However, although Vikings took to racing with enthusiasm, they were not the first occupants of Britain to be involved with the sport. The Celts who migrated from mainland Europe to Ireland enjoyed racing and the Asturian and Garrano ponies they brought with them from what is now the Iberian Peninsula were accomplished amblers and trotters. At the summer harvest festivals of Lughnasa and the Tailteann Games, both in southern Ireland, trotting races as well as chariot races were a popular feature. The Asturian ponies' smooth action made them a comfortable ride – possibly one reason why the Romans liked them so much as, with the stirrup yet to be introduced to the Roman Empire by Hun invaders, trotters were known as *tortores* meaning torturers, or *successatus* meaning shakers. Amblers eventually became known as *palfreys* in Britain, but in France the Asturian ponies, imported from Iberia, were known as *haubini* from which the word *hobbye* was derived, and it is significant that the most renowned Irish indigenous breed for centuries was known as the Irish Hobby. It is probable that it was from Garrano ponies, imported into Scotland by the early Celts, that the term *garron*, which was later to mean a gelding or work pony, derived.

Some of the Norsemen who settled in Ireland eventually migrated back to mainland Britain over subsequent generations, bringing with them people of unmixed Irish descent who had thrown in their lot with the 'white strangers', as they called the Norsemen. They settled mainly in the north of England. The significance of these early Irish immigrants was that they brought with them the stamp of indigenous Irish pony known as a *capaill* from the old Irish word for a pony. The Viking version of the word was *kapall* and by Chaucer's time, when he spelt the word 'capul', it referred to a recognized type of animal, a forebear of the Irish Hobby, as well as a pack pony. The origins of these Irish ponies are somewhat obscure, although there were indigenous ponies in Ireland before Man appeared there around 9,000 years ago, there being no evidence of human habitation in Ireland prior to this date. Scientists have established that the early Irish horses stood up to 14 hands (142 cm), larger than their contemporaries in mainland Britain, probably on account of the better quality grazing. However, another contributory factor may have been discovered during archaeological excavations in Craigiewarren Crannog in County Antrim, where old horse bones including skulls similar to the modern Arab horse have been unearthed, suggesting early foreign imports that may have influenced the size of the indigenous population.

Thus, by the tenth century, a significant mix of equine types had been introduced into Britain by different peoples, whether traders or invaders. However, during the eleventh century, pretty much everything was about to change in ways that no one would have expected as a new wave of invaders landed on British shores.

Chapter 3

THE NORMANS AND THE CRUSADES

What a horse should have he did not lack,
save a proud rider on so proud a back.
WILLIAM SHAKESPEARE, VENUS AND ADONIS

In AD 1066 an army of Vikings led by the King of Norway, having won a great battle at Gate Fulford, was about to enter the City of York which had capitulated to them, when the English King Harold defeated them in an annihilating victory at Stamford Bridge, only to turn south and perish on the field of Hastings against a new enemy. Ironically, the Norman invaders were, themselves, descendants of Vikings who had overrun northern France, their origins being disguised only by their adoption of the French language and the Catholic faith, and their very name 'Normans' was a derivative of Norsemen.

However, their success in battle lay not in their ancestry but in their use of heavy cavalry – something almost, but not entirely, alien to the British form of warfare. The progenitors of their heavy horses were not altogether unknown in England because, nearly a thousand years earlier, Roman chroniclers had described the heavy war horses of Germanica, some of which had been brought over during the Roman occupation.

NORMAN MILITARY IMPORTS

Prior to the Norman invasion, successive Anglo-Saxon kings and wealthy landowners had kept studs of horses but these were, in effect, often little more than ponies. During his reign (AD 871–901), King Alfred took the unprecedented step of employing a Master of Horse to oversee his royal stud (evidence that greater importance was being given to the breeding of horses through better selection), but the improvements were slow and the foundation stock remained, for many years, the indigenous ponies. The wording of wills of that period gives clear indication that large feral herds of ponies were also maintained. The will of Wynflaed, a wealthy woman who died around AD 950 stated: 'She bequeaths to Cynelefu her share of the untamed horses which are with Edmaers...and Eadwold and his sister are to have her tame horses in common.'

At the time of the Battle of Hastings, the six destriers or heavy war horses reportedly ridden by King Harold and his brothers were exceptions to the mounts generally available to the Saxon forces, but they were almost certainly imported from continental Europe as suitable mounts for royalty and military leaders, since such animals were still not being bred in the English studs of that period. As the English army lined up against the Gallic invaders at this most decisive battle, Harold's infantry were facing 3,000 Norman knights, most of whom were mounted on European-bred heavy horses brought over to Britain solely to support the invading army. Moreover, the outcome of the battle was not only to change the British style of warfare, but would put horse-breeding high on the national agenda as it became a royal monopoly.

In fact, the Norman invasion is one of the most significant episodes in the history of the horse on British soil, not only because we know something of the types of horses imported and the likely numbers and gender, but because the scale of the importations had a tremendous influence on British breeds, the evidence of which can still be seen clearly today. William the Conqueror, a tall, corpulent man of powerful physique, was known to have ridden an Andalusian horse at the Battle of Hastings (one of two black Andalusians at his disposal), but it is unlikely that many others in his army could have afforded one, as the Andalusian was the most revered and therefore expensive warhorse of the time. The Andalusian of the eleventh century was the ideal blend of both cold and oriental blood, a 'destrier', but with some quality to match its strength, docility and easy paces. (The term destrier comes from the Latin word *dextrarius*, meaning to be led by the right hand and referring to the knight's squire who led the stallion between battlefields while the knight rode a 'palfrey' or saddle-horse in order to save the destrier for more demanding work.) Less prestigious chargers for other officers, as well as swift mounts for messengers, draught animals and mules were brought over from France at the time, but it was substantial troop horses that made up the larger part of the thousands of horses ferried across the English Channel to form the largest cavalry command ever assembled in Britain in pre-medieval times.

The Norman heavy cavalry horses were direct descendants of the European 'Forest' horses, and impressive animals to English eyes. Over the next few hundred years, selective breeding on the fertile sandy lowlands of northern coastal Europe was to produce a further increase in height and, more importantly, substance to develop the weight and power that made them a weapon in themselves. Ridden at a lumbering trot or slow hand-gallop in a line against infantry, the intention was that they trampled and dispersed the enemy and, with this in mind, in later times they were often shod with heavy studded shoes. The common term 'to ride rough-shod' dates back to this practice. From the start, the destriers' weight-carrying ability made it possible for their riders to protect themselves in chain-mail and, ultimately, plate armour. The latter, although increasing the overall weight carried tremendously by late medieval times, making the horses slower-moving as a result, did nothing to detract from their effectiveness in a charge against enemy lines, when speed was secondary to sheer weight.

The Bayeux Tapestry, which was created to celebrate and detail the Norman victory at the Battle of Hastings, is probably the most important pictorial image from the eleventh century, partly as an outstanding example of medieval art but, more significantly, for the detailed historical evidence it provides. Although created by English embroiderers working in Winchester or Canterbury, it was commissioned by Duke William of Normandy's half-brother, Bishop Odo, to display in his new cathedral in Bayeux. It details the craftsmen constructing the vessels that would carry the invading forces and their horses, their unloading at Pevensey Bay, the stamp of horses, the saddlery, and the style of riding and warfare as the Norman soldiers in their chain-mail and helmets with distinctive nose-guards rode into battle carrying their light lances overarm like spears. (The stouter lance of the later Middle Ages was carried underarm with the full momentum of the horse behind it, and the high pommel and cantle of the later saddles prevented the rider from being dislodged and equally unable to disengage himself from his horse in the event of a fall.) Of the 202 horses depicted in the tapestry, all the Norman horses were stallions, but none were anything like the massive, over-muscled horses fictitiously portrayed in later works of art. Judging from the position of the riders' feet in relation to the lower line of the horses (and even bearing in mind the straight-legged riding position of the Norman cavalryman, who was unlikely to be much over 5ft 6 in [1.68 m] in height himself), either the comparative proportions of the tapestry's subjects were inaccurate or the horses were neither as tall nor as heavy as generally believed. Excavated bones testify that most, in reality, stood well under 15 hands (152.5 cm). However, in comparison to the working ponies of the defeated English, the Norman horses were very much *horses* – although this size difference portrayed on the tapestry may have been emphasized by its creators to enhance the supremacy of the victors over the vanquished.

Regarding the origins and breeding of the imported heavy cavalry horses, it is quickly evident that they belonged to a widespread *type* recognizable as the ancestor of the Ardennes, Flemish, Flanders, Friesian, Percheron, Holstein and other breeds, but still subject to considerable regional variation.

THE AFTERMATH OF HASTINGS: CHANGES TO AGRICULTURAL AND HORSE-BREEDING PRACTICES

Following the invasion, the Normans' influence on the indigenous equine stock was not related solely to the type of horses they imported, but also to their breeding practices and, less directly, to their fierce reprisals that followed local uprisings. Prior to the Norman Conquest, the weakness of the traditional Anglo-Saxon method of horse-breeding lay in its complete reliance on a 'survival of the fittest' policy, whereby those animals which survived the elements, poor grazing and predators including wolves (which could and did take weakly foals, or old or sickly animals), became the future breeding stock. While this might guarantee hardiness, stamina and resourcefulness, it set no standards for conformation, quality, or that most valued attribute, size. There were no attempts made to breed selectively outside of the few royal studs or private breeding enclosures of wealthy landowners and, as only stallions were ridden and the Norse practice of gelding was slow to gain wide acceptance, there were still far too many entires of inferior quality kept as riding horses, with the inherent possibility that they might becoming breeding stallions either by design or accident. Inadvertent inbreeding was probably commonplace, with the resultant loss of hybrid vigour and negative consequences in terms of reduced size, stamina and fertility over subsequent generations.

Following the Norman Conquest, a number of ill-conceived uprisings, mainly along the east coast and in the north, not only failed to halt the invaders but led instead to reprisals, the severity of which devastated great areas of the country, especially in the north of England where the reprisals were later referred to as the 'Harrying of the North'. Traditionally, prior to the invasion, the land belonging to each manor was laid out in a system of concentric circles, those fields at the centre and close to the settlement being used for arable crops, with sheep grazing the fields left fallow on the three-year rotation system which operated until post-medieval times. To the outside of these came permanent pasture grazed by milk cows or working oxen after a hay crop had been taken from it, and beyond that was common land grazed by store cattle or 'dry' cows. Any woodland bordering the common land had little agricultural value except for foraging pigs, and the moorland and rough grazing beyond, often referred to as the 'waste', was reserved for horses and goats as both were less vulnerable to attack by wolves than most other domesticated stock and could be tended by boys armed with sticks. An enclosure or 'close' in the middle of the settlement was used for holding the riding and work horses, mainly stallions.

Partly as general policy, and more specifically in response to uprisings and unrest, the invaders were ruthless in stamping Norman rule on Britain. They laid waste to large areas of the country by ransacking villages, razing buildings to the ground, burning crops and killing or driving off any available stock – which generally included the horses in the close, as they were needed to carry off anything of value the Norman soldiers had purloined. In order to cripple the economy to discourage resistance, unwanted stock was usually slaughtered, which included a culling of large numbers of inferior stallions. The brood mares and young stock on the rough grazing at the edges of the manors were left, as the troopers concentrated their efforts on the actual settlements and did not have the time or inclination to gather up the stock on marginal land. Those villagers who escaped death were left with no means of supporting themselves and, fearing further Norman raids, took refuge on higher ground or in dense woodland or fenland, where they felt safer. What farmsteads and arable land remained serviceable after the fury of the Normans had passed was almost exclusively Church property, as the Normans had orders not to molest the tenants of monastic houses whose complicity in the uprisings could not be proved. However, orders were not always followed and even the dispossessed Anglo-Saxons were not averse to robbery to supplement their meagre incomes. Reduced to foraging for food as their forebears had done, their only stock consisted of goats and ponies and both now became a source of food themselves.

The eating of horse meat had been common in Britain at one time but had become associated with the pagan cults of Odin and Freya through the Viking-introduced sport of stallion fighting. As mentioned earlier, this was relatively short-lived as an entertainment in Britain, although it survived much later in Iceland and Scandinavia – and as late as the nineteenth century an Irish observer recorded a form of stallion fighting not uncommon at that time: 'At Mullinavat in Kilkenny there was an old stone cross to which, at the horse fair, two rival owners of Irish Draught stallions would at time tender them [put them forward] and let them fight, and the one which showed the greatest courage influenced the demand for his services.' However, the consumption of horse meat retained its pagan stigma and monks in the late eleventh century recorded with horror that people in the wilderness were forced by starvation to eat it. One result was that, as poorer quality stock would be culled for meat first, it initiated the next step of selective breeding on a more general scale. When recolonization of the abandoned settlements began, the scarcity of oxen compelled people to use ponies more for agricultural work and haulage.

In both English and Norman society, land confiscated from the original owners and appropriated to Norman supporters in return for their services and loyalty was the defining currency. To help secure the Norman position on British soil and discourage possible uprisings from the displaced locals, a careful distribution of land and estates was implemented, in places of strategic importance, to favoured supporters of William the Conqueror. Bishop Odo, who acted as regent when William was out of the country, was given most of the area now known as Kent (which included the strategic port of Dover and the city of Canterbury) while Vitalis, the man who brought news of Harold's approach to Hastings, was granted land in the Whitstable area north of Canterbury. Wadard, depicted in the Bayeux Tapestry organizing supplies for the Norman landing, was similarly rewarded for his role, and other trusted nobles were granted lands in other parts of the country. The new Norman landowners were each responsible for building a castle as a stronghold and suppressing any pockets of resistance. Thus a network of Norman castles began appearing across the British landscape from Windsor in the south to Pickering in the North. Along with the distribution of land to loyal nobles went the responsibility for supporting military forces who, in turn, needed horses, and those Norman warhorses or destriers which had survived Hastings were distributed to two main groups of recipients, the *castleries*, as they were to become known, being one.

The second group of recipients of the horses dispersed from William's cavalry were the monastic houses of the Cistercian and Premonstratensian Orders set up, like the castles, with grants of land in strategic parts of the country. With their reputations as practical agricultural managers, the monks were ideally placed to take on another responsibility allocated to the Norman landowners, which was to bring back into cultivation vast tracts of land for arable use and stock grazing. With the Norman forces to support, there was good reason for this as the *Anglo-Saxon Chronicle* records: 'People wondered how this country could maintain all that army. And the King had all the army dispersed all over the country among his vassals, and they provisioned the army each in proportion to his land.' Only by rebuilding the economy and increasing agricultural output could William maintain the army he needed to ensure the security of his newly won kingdom. As for those areas left abandoned, the *Domesday Book*, that great record of English land-owning which was compiled around 1086 using the evidence of at least 62,000 witnesses, is bleakly explicit when it tells how a certain manor worth a specific rent in the days when Edward the Confessor was alive: '*…et nunc vasta est…vast est*' ('lies waste now'). But it was on these wastelands that the ancestors of the British native breeds were largely forced to survive along with their landless owners, consolidating the inherent qualities of hardiness and resilience that characterized them both.

The *Domesday Book*, so called because it purportedly brought doom and gloom to those liable to pay tax to their Norman king, is a remarkable document, recording the size of a township, the acreage of its ploughland, pasture and woodland, an inventory of all livestock, the rent it had once been worth and the rent it was assessed at in 1086. William the Conqueror's commissioners who undertook the survey went to each township accompanied by a scribe, a priest who was responsible for translating the evidence from English into the Latin in which it was recorded, and three guards. A typical example was Brandona, a manor to the north of Exmoor now known as Brendon, awarded to a Norman, Radulf de Felghere, for his services to King William. The *Domesday Book* entry for Brendon Manor records not only the extent of Radulf's land but also his stock: 'One pack-horse and a hundred and four unbroken horses, and twenty-five head of cattle, and eight swine, and a hundred sheep and thirty goats.' The large number of unbroken horses would suggest they were free-living native ponies, in this case Exmoor ponies, the term 'horse' being used for all equines regardless of size up until the nineteenth century. The existence of other herds of wild ponies in specific parts of the country is verified by other entries in the *Domesday Book* as well as in wills and the inventories of stock that often accompanied them.

The monastic houses, particularly those of the Cistercian Order, promoted the keeping of sheep, using the French system which laid equal emphasis on the production of cheese from ewes' milk as on wool as a crop. They pioneered the keeping of sheep on upland grazing but this could only be accomplished if predators (wolves especially), and herbivores which would compete with the sheep for the available grazing were eliminated, and it was the responsibility of the ecclesiastical landlords to undertake this duty. The abbots and priors not only rode out themselves in pursuit of the wolf, wildcat and deer, they also employed professional 'wolvers' and for this activity they needed suitable horses. As the wolf population dwindled (eventually to extinction in most parts by the sixteenth century – although the last British wolf was allegedly shot in Scotland as late as 1743) more sheep were kept on the high ground, necessitating horses for the shepherds and their overseers. At shearing time, horses were needed to transport the wool to the nearest ports for export, while others were needed for agricultural work, general transport and riding, meaning that all the monastic houses were compelled to maintain large stables. Each 'grange', or outlying farm specifically with a grain store, belonging to a monastic house, kept on average twelve to fifteen horses each – sometimes more depending on the size of the sheep flocks maintained and the distances to be travelled to ports or markets. The exploitation of the mineral wealth of Wales and the north of England, including lead, iron ore and coal, although practised since before Roman times, was also promoted by the monks and again demanded large numbers of pack horses.

The first Cistercian Abbey in Britain was Waverley Abbey, founded in 1128, and over the next century it was joined by around a further hundred monasteries from Balmerino in Fife to Cleve Abbey in Somerset and Tintern Abbey on the English/Welsh border. With few exceptions, Whitby Abbey in Yorkshire being one, the monks bred their own horses and they bred a variety of types for specific purposes. Their foundation stock included some destriers, and they also inherited some native pony stock with the lands they were allotted by King William, and others were acquired through gift or 'heriot', or were left to the monks in wills. (This last practice preceded the Norman invasion: as early as AD 1000, the will of a landowner named Wulfric included the grant of '…a hundred wild horses and sixteen tame geldings' to the monastery at Burton.) Through selective breeding the monks developed strains of palfreys for general riding on business, hawking and hunting (the name being derived from the Latin word *paraveredus* meaning a relay horse); cobs or 'rouncies', which were the lowest order of riding horse, for use by reeves or estate managers as well as wolvers and shepherds; and pack horses or 'capuls', for which the monasteries became renowned. (Whitby Abbey, the ruins of which overlook the town, developed a thriving trade supplying salted fish in large hampers to inland settlements and it is recorded that in 1394 the abbey maintained a stable of 63 capuls specifically for the purpose.)

Because of the trend throughout medieval times for recording the *purpose* of a horse rather than its *breed*, there is little evidence of the ancestral origins of these types, or even whether they conformed to any sort of standard. For example, the famous chronicler, Sir John Froissart, private secretary to Edward III's queen, left accurate descriptions of innumerable wars and tournaments between around 1320 and 1399, but he only described horses with any detail once when he wrote: 'The knights and their squires are mounted on large bay horses, the common people on little Galloways', the latter reference being to the renowned ponies of south-west Scotland. A century later, in 1479, the *Boke of St. Albans,* a compendium of medieval learning, mentions a number of separate breeds and types of dogs, but no distinct breeds of horses are mentioned.

This situation is further compounded by the use of a range of terms often meaning the same thing, or easily misinterpreted. For example, the term 'courser', which came into the equestrian vocabulary during medieval times, actually meant a warhorse originally, before its usage was widened to include hunting and the coursing of hares and eventually racing, the name coming from tournaments when the charge was called a 'course'. Palfreys or light riding horses were also called 'nags', especially in Scotland, 'hobbies' (although this term eventually came to represent a distinct smaller type, the Irish Hobby) and, if they paced as so many did, 'amblers' or 'pacers'. (These two terms did not then have the distinct, definitive meaning they later acquired and seem, in many cases, to have been used interchangeably.) The word 'nag', derived from the Anglo-Saxon *hnegan,* meaning to neigh, was the term used from early times for a riding horse, although documentary references to 'Scotch Nags' would indicate that they may have been a distinct and recognizable type from the thirteenth century onward. The Normans introduced their own word, *haquene,* which had the same meaning as 'nag', and the combination of the two, first latinized into *hakeneius* then anglicized into 'hackney', resulted in a word in common use from the twelfth century for what the Reverend Samuel Pegge, a Norfolk antiquarian writing in 1807, described as 'a common horse for all purposes of riding', although Samuel Johnson, in his dictionary, described a hackney as a pacing horse. Reverting to Sir John Froissart, he stated that the less wealthy Scottish soldiers were 'mounted upon little Hackneys that were never tied up…but turned, immediately after the day's march, to pasture on heath or in the fields'. Elsewhere, he uses the terms 'Galloway' and 'Hackney' alternately to mean the same type of small riding horse used by the Scottish army. Although 'Hackney' was a term much more common in the south of England than in Scotland, Froissart was himself based in London so he would have been familiar with it. Other terms in use from the early medieval period onward included 'curtals', which were 'cut-tails' or docked horses usually used as capuls or 'sumpters' for pack work. 'Double trotting horses' were simply destriers capable of carrying two riders, like the one upon which Elizabeth I rode behind her Master of Horse on more than one occasion, while 'gambading' horses were showy animals trained to prance and high-step. At the ascension of Elizabeth I, her henchmen (the term derived from the old Saxon word *hengst* meaning stallion and used to describe the squire known as the stallion-man or *hengstman* who led the knight's destrier), 'gambaded' around her, doing high-school airs.

'Running horses' were originally not racehorses but riding horses which moved laterally. A superior type of palfrey, which commanded a much higher price than its contemporaries, was the 'rakker', which neither trotted nor paced but placed its feet down one at a time: near hind, near fore, off fore and off hind (the same *sequence* as walk, but with different speed and rhythm), producing a smooth rolling motion originally called rocking, hence their name. Horses which rack are common in Iceland, where the gait is called the *tølt,* and it is possible that horses that performed this gait were introduced into Britain by Scandinavian invaders. The market for trained rakkers was very lucrative: they commanded high prices and advertisements for them appeared in the better quality London news sheets like the *Gentleman's Magazine* as late as the 1680s before the market moved over to carriage horses as a means of showing its wealth and status.

To revert to the type of pack horse known as the capul, it was the monastic orders of northern Yorkshire that were particularly successful in breeding it in medieval times, and in that area, for reasons explained in the next chapter, it eventually became known as the 'Chapman horse'. In old documents, these horses were sometimes referred to as 'curtailed' horses, implying that they were usually docked – and most were geldings as they were easier to manage in a pack line. Had the breeding stock of these horses been kept on upland grazing, they would have reduced in both size and substance over ensuing generations to something akin to their native pony ancestors. Instead, the monks maintained the size and stamp of their horses by keeping them on the better quality valley grazing in the *riddings*, or clearings in woodland, from which the term North Riding of Yorkshire is derived. Some of the *riddings* were the gift of generous local landowners, while other patrons donated annual grazing rights to the abbeys in the form of certain numbers of sheep allowed on the moors. (While specific grants of horse grazing are mentioned in the records, they were never on open moorland.)

While the monastic houses may have taken on the breeding of many classes of horses, the breeding of warhorses was essentially a royal monopoly. A succession of monarchs initiated studs and breeding programmes in the belief that national security would depend on being able to field an army of heavily armoured knights mounted on such animals. William the Conqueror was recorded as having imported horses of the Flanders breed, and later Richard the Lionheart (reigned 1189–1199) continued the trend by importing examples of a number of heavy continental types including the Brabançon, a Belgian draught breed, while his successor, the unpopular King John, was credited with importing one hundred 'chosen stallions of the Flanders breed and thus mainly contributed to prepare our noble breed of draught horses', according to one writer. In 1205 Henry II imported two stallions from Lombardy, and around 1290 Edward I set up a network of studs across England to supply the remount depots of his army, while his successor, Edward II, introduced Flemish horses with the intention of producing Britain's own breed of 'greate horse', eventually to become known as the Old English Black. In 1311, he also brought to Britain thirty Lombardy warhorses, and twelve heavy draught stallions from the same area. In 1328 his son, Edward III, issued an edict prohibiting the exportation of any British horses at the same time as he imported fifty stallions from Spain. The horses were bred under the care of the *Custodes Equorum Regis* or Keeper of the King's Horses in large royal parks like Guildford, Woodstock and Windsor where, on average, around twenty-five brood mares would be maintained. They were covered by stallions, also Crown property, which were rotated around the royal parks every few seasons to bring in fresh blood. This often necessitated long journeys between castles and consequently, during Edward II's reign, stallions from Tutbury in Staffordshire and Merton in Surrey were recorded as having also been used at Pickering in Yorkshire.

Although 'great horses' were used almost exclusively for military purposes, some occasional personal use is also recorded. When Edward II travelled from London to York in 1326 to go hunting, his carriage was drawn by six 'great' horses. The accounts for Edward II's stud at Pickering Castle in Yorkshire show that 'great horses' were very expensive to maintain, eating 20 lb (9 kg) of oats each per day. Even an archbishop writing in 1310 denounced the excessive cost of their keep, with each horse costing the outrageous sum of two shillings and seven pence a week 'which would keep four or five poor people', while the groom's extravagant wages came to three-and-a-half pence a day. These destriers were totally unsuited for hunting – the main principal recreational activity of the military when off duty – but the sport of jousting, introduced originally as battle training, did give them another string to their bow.

IMPORTS FROM THE CRUSADES

If the Norman invasion had an influence on the development of horse breeds in Britain, then so did another military venture. For a period from the last years of the eleventh century, knights from Britain (primarily Norman) became embroiled in the challenge of trying to take Jerusalem back from the Muslims and protecting Christian pilgrims from attack in the

Holy Land. The Crusades bolstered the breeding of warhorses in many parts of Europe, including England, but they also had a secondary influence on the equine population as knights returning from duty brought home with them horses of oriental blood, usually stallions, as the age-old custom of riding only entires persisted, even if their Muslim adversaries often favoured mares. Although many of the horses brought back from the Crusades would have been captured in battle, King Richard I ('the Lionheart') was actually presented with two 'most noble Arab horses' by his chivalrous opponent, Saladin, and he is purported to have sent these back to England.

In this era, Normandy had the same reputation for horse-breeding in France as Yorkshire had in England, and the Abbeys in Normandy and

Welsh Section C and D Cobs were both bred up from Welsh Mountain ponies with the addition of destrier, Hackney, Andalusian and other blood.

Brittany were apparently well-stocked with horses of Arab type owing to the generosity of homecoming Crusaders like Vicomte de Rohan, who brought nine such horses back with him. These imports served to bolster stock both in Normandy and Britain (including Ireland) since French-bred horses of eastern blood were regularly shipped over to Britain by Norman landowners – who also imported other foreign stock for their own purposes. Robert de Belesme, Count of Shrewsbury, whose father had commanded part of the Norman cavalry at Hastings, imported a number of Spanish stallions to his Welsh estates, these horses being described by the Archdeacon of Brecon as 'remarkable for their majestic proportion and astonishing fleetness'. These Spanish horses, the ancestors of the modern Andalusians as well as many other European breeds, were destriers, but with considerably more quality and style than the general stamp of Norman warhorse and, in the case of the de Belesme estates, they probably had considerable influence in the development of the modern Welsh Cob.

With Britain flooded by foreign imports, it might have been expected that the native ponies of Britain would have struggled to survive but, partly owing to the low esteem in which they were held, they managed to retain their identity while the new imports were about to launch the beginnings of the British horse breeds.

Chapter 4

THE ASCENT OF
THE HORSE

*No nation in Europe is more backward and
careless in breeding and managing horses
than we are in England.*
J. CROUCH, 1636

Throughout the Middle Ages, there were basically three types of equine indispensable to the everyday life of the nation: horses for general riding, pack horses and horses for military use, and the breeding of all three proliferated as Britain became increasingly dependent on the horse for transport, commerce and matters of national security. Within these generic categories there was considerable variation of type according to localized needs, which supported the increasing development of emerging regional breeds.

THE DECLINE OF THE DESTRIER AND THE
EMERGENCE OF HORSE FAIRS

Although the breeding of 'great horses' began to wane from the fourteenth century onward, the demise of the heavy destrier had really started a couple of centuries earlier, during the Crusades, when the mounted knights in armour, a slow and not very manoeuvrable unit, had found themselves no match for the swift Saracens on fast, agile oriental horses. Unencumbered by heavy armour, Saladin's cavalry had quickly demonstrated the efficacy of their style of warfare, whereas European armour had become so heavy and cumbersome that, as one acute observer noted, 'It protects the wearer and prevents him from injuring others.' In 1314, at Bannockburn, Robert the Bruce and an army of around 8,800 men had routed Edward II's 29,000 men, 4,000 of whom were armoured knights on destriers. However, in mainland Europe the destrier continued to dominate the battlefield and it was not until the English longbow, then gunpowder and more effective firearms, had become integral parts of warfare, making the outdated and slow-moving mounted knight an easy target, that there was a shift of emphasis in the European studs. At this point, the breeding of destriers slowly diminished as a lighter, more versatile stamp of troop horse began to take their place and, over time, many of the remaining destriers were sold off. In England, William Wykeham, Edward III's Surveyor of the King's Work at Windsor Castle, used the proceeds of the sale of the Windsor 'great horses' to help fund new construction work at the castle. From this point, destrier blood became so predominant in the breeding of working horses (culminating ultimately in such breeds as the Shire and Suffolk), that the Midlands cart horse of the eighteenth century was not substantially different from the tournament horse of the fifteenth.

As mentioned in the previous chapter, since Anglo-Saxon times, manors had maintained semi-feral herds of ponies on common uplands, which had to be gathered annually to be marked in some way to indicate ownership, often by brands or nicks in the ears, and to separate the young stock for sale. Tenants on ecclesiastically owned land were required, under the agreement of their tenure, to work a specified number of days (known as 'boon days') for their landlords, and the work generally included the gathering of the landlord's free-ranging stock. The sales that usually followed these gatherings were the forerunners of the organized horse fairs which soon began to take place regularly in various parts of the country as the demand for horses escalated. As early as 1171 a monk, William Fitzstephen, writing an account of the city of London, gave a brief but much-quoted description of the weekly horse sale held on a *campus planus* or smooth field, now known as Smithfield, just outside one of the city gates. He mentioned the fact that all kinds of horses were sold there every Friday, including ambling palfreys, cobs suitable for squires, pack horses, mares for ploughing and draught work (some in-foal or with foals at foot), well-bred young stock, and destriers, which he describes as 'expensive chargers of handsome conformation and impressive height, switching their ears and arching their necks: they have massive quarters'. His words emphasize both the diversity and availability of a range of different types available at the time which, by the nineteenth century, would have developed into many of the breeds we recognize today.

THE STATUTES OF HENRY VIII

Despite this apparent picture of a thriving horse population, very little goes smoothly through the course of history and during his reign (1485–1509), the Tudor monarch Henry VII let the importance of the royal studs slip, partially because of his thriftiness with the privy purse which left a full Treasury on his death, but also because he was less interested in horse-breeding than his predecessors had been. He also had little interest in hunting deer and in 1508 leased Exmoor Forest, once a royal deer park, to its warden, Sir Thomas Carew, for grazing.

When his son, Henry VIII succeeded him, a record of the royal stables at the time lists over 100 horses including: '30 coursers, 12 running horses, 4 Barbary horses, 8 stallions, 12 Hobbies and geldings, 1 mail horse, 3 battle horses, 1 stalking horse, 1 pack horse, 7 sumpters and 5 horses for the carriage of robes.' In addition, there were ten horses for the officers of the Master of the Horse and, under the heading of 'Hackneys of Diverse Officers', even a horse for the King's fool. While this does not immediately suggest a dearth of horses, it may be that the new monarch foresaw such a situation developing, for he attempted, in his rash and clumsy way, to remedy what he saw as the degeneration of Britain's horses by using the law to define a national horse-breeding policy. His policy may have been partly motivated by personal reasons for, as the Venetian ambassador noted in 1519, the corpulent monarch never went hunting 'but he tired eight or ten horses which he picked up along the way'. Furthermore, from a military perspective, when in full armour he is said to have weighed in at 400 lb (182 kg).

With reference to this military perspective, it has to be said that Henry's oft-quoted laws concerning the breeding of horses on common ground were not intended to promote the breeding of 'great horses' (as is so often assumed), but were a genuine, if misguided, attempt to ensure a plentiful supply of hardy, versatile animals of 14–15 hands (142–152.5 cm) which, unlike the destrier, could be used for civilian as well as military purposes. Relating back to Henry VII's thriftiness with the royal purse, it should be understood that to field a mounted knight ready for battle had necessitated a retinue consisting of a palfrey for the knight to ride when not in battle, a squire on a cob to lead the destrier, and at least one attendant to take charge of the two pack horses needed to carry the armour, weapons and other equipment. Thus, as a fighting unit, the mounted knight was phenomenally expensive. Moreover, under feudal law it was incumbent on the taxpayers to help fund the armed forces, and in the Midlands and south of England it was often a matter of several manors taking collective responsibility to put one man on the battlefield. Further north, where a high proportion of ecclesiastically owned land was tenanted 'in consideration of military service' (i.e. in lieu of rent), the 'loan' of requisitioned horses was sometimes taken a stage further and there is evidence of the English forces being commanded by generals like the Bishop of Durham or the Abbot of Fountains. Throughout Tudor times, as before, the farming of land on military tenure meant that tenants, if called upon, had to muster *'with horse and harneys'*. The *'harneys'* (harness) was not to go on the horse; it referred to the arms and equipment of the man, and the tenants' horses were usually native pony types used for haulage or farm work when not on military service. When Blundeville, writing in 1565, suggested that by putting the tallest native mares to Neapolitan destriers, 'horses for service in war' should be produced, he was reiterating Henry VIII's belief that the cavalry of the future lay in troopers like the military tenants, and Henry's statutes were meant to provide them with suitable horses.

These statutes decreed that those who could afford it should find, keep and maintain a prescribed number of 'stoned trotting horses for the saddle', and the statute is specific regarding the number in relation to the owner's station in life and income. These stallions had to be three years old or over, not under 14 hands (142 cm) and, most significantly, they had to trot, as pacers and amblers were considered unsuitable for military purposes. (Of 163 horses requisitioned from the tenants of Jervaulx Abbey in 1513 for the Battle of Flodden, eighteen were amblers, sixteen were rakkers, but the majority, 129 in number, were trotters.) The statutes also decreed that those with sufficient land, meeting the necessary criteria, were required to keep brood mares of not less than 13 hands (132 cm) and capable of breeding foals, and there were clauses prohibiting the export of horses above a specified value abroad or into Scotland, with punitive fines for those who did not comply. These Acts also concerned the breeding of horses in controlled environments – parks, breeding enclosures and the like – but it was the statute passed in 1541 concerning the de-pasturing of stallions on common ground that is so often cited as the greatest threat to British native pony breeds. It stated:

> Forasmuch as the breed of good and strong horses is a great help and defence to the realm and a great comoditie to the inhabitants thereof, which is now much decayed by reason that little stoned horses and nags be suffered to pasture in forests, etc. and to cover mares feeding there, therefore for the increase of stronger horses hereafter be it enacted that no commoner or commoners within any forest, chase, moore, marish, heth, common or wast grounde at any time after the 31st March 1541 shall have or put forth to pasture in any such ground, etc. any stoned

horse or horses being above the age of two yeare and not being of the altitude and height of fifteen handfuls.

But the fact that it did not apply to Northumberland, Cumberland, Westmorland, Durham, Rutland, Hertfordshire, Derbyshire, Surrey, Sussex, Middlesex, part of Cambridge, Monmouthshire, Nottinghamshire, Dorset, Devon or Cornwall immediately limited its effects.

Another section of the King's statutes, however, decreed that all commons, chases, marshes and moors were to be gathered once a year (i.e. the stock rounded up and penned) and:

> If there shall be found any mare, filly, fole or gelding that then shall be thought not to be able or like to be able to beare foles of reasonable stature, or not able or like to grow to be profitable labours, by the discretion of the drivers aforesaid then the same drivers shall cayse the same unprofitable beastes every one of them to be killed.

Fortunately, as no specific size was mentioned, the instruction could be interpreted subjectively, and the locals tasked with the gathering were not always particularly diligent in their work, so what could have been disastrous for native pony breeds did little real harm. Trying to find the wild herds in inaccessible regions would have often rendered the exercise futile. Moreover, as history had shown, certain terrains could only support animals of a certain height so, if larger animals were turned out, they either did not survive or, if they did, their progeny reduced in size over a few generations to that appropriate to the environment. Thus, the New Forest, which has the least isolated of the native breeds' territories, has seen every kind of stallion turned out, from Arabs to Highlands, from Roman times up to the twentieth century, with the aim of 'improving' the local stock yet, as Sir Berkeley Piggott remarked, such is the 'grinding-down' effect of the forest's environment that one type alone survives at the end – and that is the one best able to maintain and reproduce itself under the local conditions.

The same principle applied in the other breeding areas, too, so it comes as no surprise to find that, as late as the mid-seventeenth century, the average size of horses, with the exception of those bred from selected stock in breeding enclosures and parks, averaged 13 hands (132 cm).

The extent to which Henry VIII's legislation succeeded in improving the availability of horses for military purposes must be open to question since, by the time his daughter, Elizabeth I, was on the throne and facing the threat of a Spanish invasion, only 3,000 cavalry horses could be mustered in the whole of England. This may explain why the coach used by the Queen for the opening of Parliament in October 1584 was drawn by six grey Hungarian horses imported four years previously, or why Lord Robert Dudley, later the Earl of Leicester, who was Elizabeth's Master of Horse, wrote to the Earl of Sussex in Ireland at one point saying that the Queen requested some Irish horses be sent over, as there was evidently a dearth of suitable English-bred horses.

REQUIREMENTS FOR GENERAL RIDING HORSES

Moving on from Henry's efforts to improve the horses available for military purposes, the criteria for the general riding horse were stamina, hardiness, inherent soundness and comfortable gaits, which, in contrast to the demands of military horses, generally meant a pacer or ambler (as explained earlier, these terms were more or less interchangeable at that time). From the distances between posting inns, which offered relays of saddle horses for the use of travellers in the days before the public coaching system, it would appear that daily journeys of up to fourteen hours were not uncommon, so a comfortable mount was essential. It was theoretically possible to breed pacing horses, and it was not difficult to train trotters to pace by the use of special hobbles. Although pacing was not a natural gait for the wild ancestors of the horse, some strains of domesticated horses showed a tendency to pace, which was further developed by training and selective breeding. On the other hand, it was relatively easy to teach a pacing horse to trot, which is why pacing has vanished almost completely, in the course of the last two centuries or so, from those breeds among which it was once a speciality.

Many of the Spanish horses imported in late Norman, Tudor and Stuart times were examples of a specialized strain of ambling courser known as the 'Spanish jennet', the name *jennet* coming from the *genista* style of riding with short stirrups favoured by Moorish light cavalrymen. As early as 1367, a Castillian chronicler had commented that when the Black Prince fought the Spanish at Najera, light horsemen or *genetors* had supported the men-at-arms in the Spanish forces, indicating that the term was military in origin long before it came to define an ambling palfrey. The thriving trade between Spain and the merchants of Galway resulted in both Andalusian horses from southern Spain and pacing jennets from northern Spain being imported into Ireland. Evidence of such imports comes from a letter written in 1668 by the Duke of Ormonde to his stud manager in Ireland that specifically mentions a Spanish horse purchased from Lord Dungannon which 'may serve to help the neighbourhood to mend the ordinary breed', suggesting some deficiencies in the local horses. (Writing in 1958 of the action of Connemara ponies, Lady Wentworth suggested that 'the old Spanish amble should in my opinion be encouraged in ponies of the Andalusian type as it is a hall-mark of their ancestry'.) A factor that possibly contributed to these deficiencies was hinted at in Robert Payne's *Brief Description of Ireland 1588 to 1590*: 'The meanest Irishman disdaineth to ride on a mare.' This would have meant that in Ireland, as in other places where stallions were favoured for riding, there would have been less inclination to geld inferior stock and their influence on the gene pool (whether intended or not) would have been largely negative.

Regarding other Spanish influences on the horses of Ireland, there is a popular myth that equine survivors of the Spanish Armada of 1588 swam ashore from shipwrecks to stamp their influence on native breeds, but there is no evidence of this. To the contrary, any horses carried on Armada ships were jettisoned on the east coast of England or Scotland as fresh water supplies for the crews ran low long before the ships rounded the northern tip of Scotland and faced the perils of the western seaboard, where so many came to grief.

An upward trend in the value of horses during the Elizabethan and early Stuart period can be gleaned from the average prices obtained at the Shrewsbury Horse Fair, one of the most important markets of the time, which attracted buyers from across western and central England. In 1560 the average price of a broken horse was 30 shillings, twenty years later it was up to 40 shillings, 50 shillings by 1610, 54 shillings by 1620, and 83 shillings by 1638.

HORSE-BREEDING IN SCOTLAND

In Scotland, horse-breeding had been given a fillip by the arrival of 'a choice collection of the best French breeds', a gift from Louis XII of France to James IV around 1510, which might indicate that there was more royal concern with horse-breeding in Scotland at that time than had been the case in England under Henry VII. Although no historical details of these imports exist, it is believed that the shipment comprised twelve 'grey horses of Normandy', ancestors of the Percheron breed which hails from that area. In 1535, King James V encouraged the improvement of the horse stock of his realm further by passing a law to increase the size of the Scottish horses, and five years later Henry VIII sent, through Sir Ralph Sadler, his ambassador to Scotland, a number of Spanish jennets and Barbary horses for the Scottish king, who used them for breeding. At the end of the sixteenth century Lord David Murray, Private Secretary to James VI of Scotland, sent a letter to the Laird of Glenorchy, thanking the Laird on behalf of the King for a pair of eagles and adding: 'according to his promise he hath sent you a horse to be a stallion, one of the best in his stable for that purpose and comendis him kyndlie to you'. It is known that, at the time, the royal stables included Spanish, Arab and Turkish horses and also that the

Lairds of Glenorchy had 'introduced English and foreign horses for their great stud in Perthshire' on previous occasions. (As late as 1554 wild ponies had still existed in that region, for one of the monks of Finlarig, the monastic institution on the banks of Loch Tay, recorded that during the great snowstorm that year 'many little wild horses and mares perished and died for want of food in the mountains and other parts'.)

The Highland garron, often erroneously referred to as a breed when it was in fact a cross-bred stamp of animal, may owe its origins to some of these imports for, as John Macdonald noted in the 1930s, 'it is more than probable that they were descended from Percheron stallions which were mated to small but useful Highland ponies'. His view was shared by a contemporary, the Duke of Atholl, himself a noted breeder of Highland ponies, who detected 'some distant but strong strain of Arab blood', which is not surprising for the Percheron contains a strong element of oriental blood in its make-up. Although the name 'garron' actually means gelding and referred to working animals which were always gelded, John Macdonald went on to note of the name: 'It is now generally applied to the strong, sturdy, small horses which hardly come under the title of ponies…as it is a product of crossing, it can hardly be called a native breed.'

HORSE-BREEDING IN IRELAND

In Ireland, as in Scotland, a 'stamp' of horse was emerging – although this was part of a protracted process going back to the years of the Norman Conquest. Prior to that time, horses described as 'small and dun-coloured' had been brought to Ireland by Celtic invaders 2,500 years ago and during subsequent centuries of struggle with invaders such as the Norsemen, the autonomous Irish rulers had been forced further and further west, taking their horses with them, so that the native stock of the most westerly lands were probably closest to the original Celtic imports. It was not until the English invasion of Ireland in 1172 that the pony population, believed by scientists to range in height at that time from 12 to 14 hands (122–142 cm), began to develop into something larger through the introduction of the ubiquitous destriers. Giraldus Cambrensis, Secretary and Chaplain to Henry II, describing the Irish horsemen who opposed the English invasion, noted that they used 'halters which serve the purpose of a bridle and bit and do not prevent the horses from feeding as they always live upon grass', implying that the indigenous ponies received no supplementary feeding despite the rigours of military duty. The influence of the invaders' horses on the native stock seems to have been fairly rapid for, as early as 1296, medieval documents refer to Irish soldiers taking horses to Scotland. The ebb and flow of international politics being what it is, in 1367 King Edward III, intending to keep English settlers and the local Irish apart, drew up the Statute of Kilkenny which banned the English from selling horses to the Irish (and thereby risking 'equipping the enemy'). However, fifty years later, in 1417–18, Henry V took Irish troops with him to France, and those that were mounted were said to ride 'excellently on small mountain horses'.

It was not long before the Irish Hobby, a generic type derived from the Celtic and English invaders' horses and recognized as the foundation stock for both the Connemara and Irish Draught breeds, was in great demand as a cavalry horse, despite the fact that, as Stainihurst verified in his *Description of Ireland*: 'Commonly they amble but not gallop and run.' Another fifteenth-century Italian visitor to Ireland, Raphael Coalternus, wrote that 'Ireland possesses nothing worthy of mention but corn and excellent horses', evidence that the reputation of Irish horses was well established at that time. The archives of Venice and Modena show that, in 1497, the Duke of Ferrara received permission from Henry VII to buy Hobbies in Ireland, resulting in twelve horses being purchased for export to Italy. In 1527, Henry VIII gave permission for the export of two Irish Hobby stallions and eight mares to the new Duke of Ferrara, third husband of the famous poisoner, Lucretia Borgia. The Duke's instructions to his envoy in Ireland were exacting:

> The mares to be young, from four to five years old and in foal, and to be procured by a man who understands about them, so that they may be purchased of fine shape and of the best sort to be got; but their coats to be of any colour except white. The two hobby stallions need not be so young, though care must be taken that they be not too old, and above all, that they may be handsome and of easy pace.

In stipulating that the horses should be 'of easy pace', the Duke specifically means amblers. Just a few years before the Duke's purchases, John Mayor, writing on Ireland in 1520 stated:

> The island produces a kind of horse which the natives call haubini, whose pace is of the gentlest. They were called Asturcones in the old times because they came from Asturi in Spain and indeed the Spanish colonists brought these horses along with them. The French call these same horses English Haubini or Hobini.

Another contemporary writer, Paulus Jovis, describing the Irish horse said: 'Most excellent horses of a very pure breed are produced, termed hobini by the English which have a most gentle pace', adding that he saw twelve white horses of this breed in the Pope's procession. It was, however, for military use that the Hobby was most highly esteemed and, by the end of the sixteenth century, they were being exported to many other European countries despite the export bans imposed on shipments of Irish horses at various points in the fifteenth, sixteenth and seventeenth centuries. The Napoleonic Wars, in the early years of the nineteenth century, were cited as one of the major factors in the decline in population of the breed. By then the Irish Hobby was so well known that the name was used for the draped wicker framework 'ridden' by morris dancers and the child's toy with a horse's head on a stick, and, to this day, an annual Hobby Horse Parade is held at Padstow in Cornwall on May Day.

BREEDS IN BRITAIN IN EARLY STUART TIMES

Some idea of the breeds, domestic and foreign, available in various parts of Britain at the turn of the sixteenth century – and the esteem in which they were generally held – can be gleaned from Nicholas Morgan's book, *Perfection of Horsemanship*, published in 1609, in which he sets out a table of breeds arranged in order of popularity in England. Of the thirteen breeds mentioned only the Irish horse (in twelfth place) is of British origin; the other breeds include the Arab in the top slot, the Andalusian in sixth place, the Flanders horse tenth and the Friesian thirteenth. However, the writer does note that England excelled in palfreys, Scotland in trotting geldings and Wales in hackneys or riding horses. Although interesting, the list is probably inaccurate in part, and the ranking should perhaps be taken with a pinch of salt, for Morgan was largely influenced by other writers and scholars and, while Thessalian horses are ranked in second place, in reality none of these famed Greek horses were actually imported into England and Morgan is basing his selection simply on their reputation. Similarly, his listing of Swedish horses in eleventh place seems suspect. During his reign, Henry VIII had banned the selling of horses above a specified value into Scotland (which carried the inherent risk that they might be used to mount an army against him). This had resulted in some Scandinavian horses being imported into Scotland but, by the time of Morgan's list, no such imports had been made into England. (Henry's ban was rescinded prior to the Union of the Crowns under James I in 1603: no longer would Scottish kings have to make written requests to the English monarch to allow them to buy English horses, as James V had been forced to do, and the trade in horses, both domestic and foreign, continued to escalate.) When it came to commenting on native breeds, Morgan did say that the horses bred 'in the North parts of this Kingdom' were of consistently high quality, and expensive. These were most probably the stamp of horse referred to elsewhere as the Yorkshire Galloway or 'breed of the north', which were bred selectively by some monastic establishments as superior riding horses and are believed by some to have later played a major role in the early development of the Thoroughbred.

THE ADVENT OF THE PACK HORSE

The commercial expansion of Britain throughout Tudor and Stuart times, coupled with increased foreign export opportunities, brought about an escalation in the transportation of goods. Improved methods of agriculture, the breeding of better quality farm stock, greater output of foodstuffs and wool, and more efficient mining for coal and various metals, produced a transport crisis that would not be alleviated until the canals and then the railways came into being. Unsuitable roads limited the use of wheeled vehicles for general transport and, as late as the eighteenth century, the harvest waggon and two-wheeled farm cart, both of which virtually needed a destrier to pull them, were the commonest vehicles in England. The solution to transporting goods lay in the use of pack horses, which had been employed locally for centuries as verified by the illustration of a Sussex pack pony being purloined by a Norman trooper in the Bayeaux Tapestry. What roads there were could only be used during the summer months for, as William Harrison had noted in 1658 in his *An Elizabethan Guide to England*, the roads were 'verie deepe and troublesome in the winter halfe'. Over a century later, Arthur Young wrote an agricultural survey of the north in which he mentions measuring ruts 4 ft (1.2 m) deep on one main road in Lancashire, and a summer storm was sufficient to turn the roads into an impassable mire of soft mud which necessitated as many as ten horses to pull a heavily loaded waggon.

The pack horse trains kept off the main roads and followed a network of green roads, 'pack-trods' and causeways, carrying every imaginable cargo and providing a reliable and effective service. Many of the operators were one-man businesses, often running their pack trains alongside farms or mills, but others were professional 'lademen', so called not because they led the horses, which were actually trained to travel loose-headed (without halters or bridles), but because of their professional skill in evenly distributing and securing the loads on each animal. There were basically two types of lademen: those who worked in a very localized area, perhaps transporting local farmers' corn to the village mill to be ground for domestic use, and those who made regular scheduled journeys between the bigger towns and ports with 'trains' of up to twenty animals. On local journeys one man might be responsible for the ten or more ponies which followed the lead of the bell-mare on which he was mounted. (Using a bell-mare – named for the bell worn around the mare's neck – as a leader, mimicked the ponies' natural herd instinct to follow a dominant animal and was not dissimilar from the use of a sheep with a bell, known as the 'bell wether' since Chaucer's time, to head a flock grazing on common ground.) On longer journeys, the ratio was more usually one man per four horses. All lademen basically used the same type of animal, what we might now call a 'cobby sort', showing the clear evidence of its native pony ancestry as well as the unmistakable influence of its imported forebears, resulting in a short-legged animal of around 14 hands (142 cm), well-built, sure-footed, quiet-natured and tireless. The height was important, for a larger animal would be difficult to load and unload each morning and evening, and a smaller animal would have a reduced carrying capacity. Two types of pack horse were sufficiently distinct to have acquired names, those of Devon and Yorkshire, the latter originally being bred by the monks of the great monastic houses like Fountains Abbey and noted for their long backs, a desirable attribute in a horse used for carrying wool, a relatively light but bulky cargo.

When, between 1534 and 1540, Henry VIII had dissolved all the monasteries and abbeys, this resulted in the ecclesiastical stock, including horses, being sold off. Although some monastic records of stock did survive, most of the vellum manuscripts of the plundered institutions were lost, and along with them the invaluable information they held on the breeding of horses. Many of the pack horses were bought by a unique class of professional lademen, itinerant traders who purchased stock including pottery from the manufacturers in Derbyshire and travelled around selling it, which resulted in many of them being known as 'potters'. Also known as 'cheapmen' for the inexpensive goods they traded, their name became synonymous with the horses they used and references to 'Chapman horses', the ancestors of the modern Cleveland Bay, were common throughout the north of England. It is claimed that when perishable goods (including fresh fish) were being carried, the pack horses trotted rather than walked (as was usual) and they could carry a 16 st (102 kg) load at an average speed of 16 miles (28 km) an hour. One early Cleveland Bay apparently hauled 700 lb (318 kg) 60 miles (96 km) in 24 hours four times a week, a fact triumphantly publicized in later years by the Cleveland Bay Society who pointed out: 'Elephants and camels can be found to carry the weight, but how long would they take to do the four journeys?'

One significant factor in the development of some pack horse breeds is that the white-robed Cisterican monks were known to have favoured white-coloured livestock, such as the breed of white cattle now known as British Whites, produced by the monks of Whalley Abbey in Lancashire. With the dissolution of the monasteries there was an immediate proliferation of grey horses in the equine population around the sites of Cistercian houses, which introduced grey as a colour into some emerging breeds and helped to establish it in others where it already existed. Thus, grey was introduced into the Dales and Fell ponies and possibly into the Shire but, curiously, not into the Chapman horse which was allegedly always 'traditionally bay in colour'. (If this is so, then the grey mare that caused controversy when she won the Cleveland Bay brood mare class at Whitby Show in 1860 was certainly not a pure-bred.)

Another factor in the refinement of pack horse types and breeds was rooted in a increased interest in European travel. Since the reign of Elizabeth I, the sons of wealthy families had been encouraged to travel abroad on educational excursions (the forerunners of what would become the grand tours of Europe), to visit famous cities and historical sites and to collect works of art, sculptures, furniture, artefacts and, quite often, horses.

Many returned with Arab or Barbary horses which could be purchased relatively cheaply on the docks at ports like Marseilles and ridden part of the way home by grooms – which says much for the qualities of these North African imports considering the distances involved, the state of the roads and the standard of stabling and forage at the wayside inns where they lodged. It was reported that many Barb horses were brought into the port of Whitby on the North Yorkshire coast. Another source of high-quality imports came with the death of Elizabeth I in 1603, for her successor, James I, was keen to re-establish links with Catholic Spain (lost during the previous two monarchs' reigns), and the reward for his diplomatic efforts included, amongst other things, the gift of a large number of Andalusian horses from the Royal Cordoba Stud founded by King Philip of Spain in 1571. These horses became the responsibility of the King's Master of the Horse, The Duke of Buckingham who, in 1620, acquired the extensive Helmsley estate in Yorkshire through his prudent marriage to Lady Katherine Manners. He took most of the Andalusian horses up into Yorkshire, where they were crossed with the local stock and ultimately absorbed into what would become the Cleveland Bay and also the Yorkshire Trotter, an all-round utility riding horse, able to trot long distances at speed, and with the low, ground-covering action peculiar to that class of horse.

THE DEVELOPMENT OF HEAVY FARM BREEDS

During the same period, the heavy draught horses of Lincolnshire and Cambridgeshire, descendants of the old destrier, had considerable influence on improving the heavy horses in other parts of the country. However, in the Norfolk area, where the increasingly defunct destriers had been redeployed on the land, they developed into a stamp of farm horse known as the Norfolk Black, Norfolk Farm Horse or Black Fen Horse which, according to John Marshall in his book *The Rural Economy of Norfolk,* published in 1787: 'stood hard work and hard keep in a remarkable manner'. These were not big horses and lacked the bone and substance of some other heavy horse breeds, but they were active trotters and, according to John Lawrence in his *Philosophical and Practical Treatise on Horses,* published in 1796, were 'well-fitted both for the saddle and draught'.

In the eighteenth and early nineteenth century, Dutch drainage and land reclamation experts were to bring to the Norfolk area black trotting horses, that is Friesian horses which by then had been transformed from the medieval destrier-type into a stylish road horse through the addition of Andalusian and other blood. (The ancestors of these Friesians had already found favour in the area in earlier times: in 1558, Thomas Blundeville, who was born and lived in Norfolk, alluded to the popularity of the Friesian in his book *The Foure Chiefest Offices of Horsemanship,* although, like other writers of the time, he made little mention of British breeds.) In addition to these Low Countries imports, horses of eastern blood were also finding their way into the Norfolk region. Typical was the advertisement in the *Norfolk Mercury* in April 1741 for: 'A famous stallion, an Arabian, by the size fifteen hands three inches, and strength proportioned', which was large for an Arab – if, indeed, it was that size. By crossing these imports with the native farm mares, a stamp of utility riding horse known as the Norfolk Trotter or Roadster (similar to the Yorkshire Trotter) was developed, both of which were to play major roles in the development of the Hackney horse.

INFLUENCE OF THE DROVERS

Another side effect of greater agricultural output in Britain was the appearance of Scottish cattle drovers, who regularly travelled into England to trade Kyloe cattle at the well-known fairs and sales held throughout the north. As cities began to expand rapidly from the late eighteenth century on, the drovers' excursions took them down the country as far as Manchester, Birmingham and London, using the old roads like the

Gallowgate, a green road which wound its way south from the Scottish borders. Like their contemporaries, the border reivers (professional livestock thieves whose raids mirrored those of their Pictish ancestors), many drovers were reportedly mounted on Scotch Galloways, the renowned and tireless breed of south-west Scotland. As traders, the drovers were not averse to horse-dealing and Galloway blood was undoubtedly introduced to many other parts of Britain so that the term 'Galloway' came to denote an agile, tireless and hardy stamp of general utility pony rather than necessarily an example of the Scottish breed. R. Harrington's 1865 painting of a Galloway belonging to John Richardson, a noted Cumberland breeder of Galloways, shows a breedy type of pony of not more than 14 hands (142 cm), displaying many Arab characteristics, proof of the unspecific use of the term by then.

Not only Scottish but also Welsh cattle drovers made regular trips into England, usually to the east coast, and they were responsible for distributing the blood of the Welsh Cob types upon which they were mounted, sometimes referred to as Welsh Cart Horses or Powys Cobs, to other parts of Britain. The ancestry of these cobs can be traced to native Welsh pony mares and imported European stallions. Of greater significance, however, was the fact that Norfolk Roadster blood, from which the modern Hackney horse developed, was introduced back into Wales by the drovers either returning with stallions they had bought or traded or by getting the Welsh mares they were mounted on covered by Roadster stallions while they were in the eastern counties. (Significantly, both Welsh Cobs and Hackneys were registered in the same stud book in the early years.)

THE RISE OF RACING

Another major influence on the development of the horse was the sport of racing. As mentioned earlier, racing as a sport in the British Isles has existed in various forms since Roman times, the first recorded race having apparently taken place at Netherby in Cumbria in AD 210 between horses imported by the Roman emperor, Lucius Septimus Severus. Excavated floor mosaics from the third and fourth centuries AD clearly show riders on ponies taking part in some form of competitive race. Later references to racing include details of a match between two Arabs over a seven-mile (11.25 km) course in London in 957, and two centuries later the races were still as long but now often included a minimum weight stipulation of 12 st (76 kg) and horses had to be six years old or over. In 1117 a new course devoted solely to horse racing was built at Smithfield and the monk, Fitzstephen, writing in 1170, mentions the Smithfield Horse Fair and the geldings 'whom the buyers do specially regard for pace and swiftness'. He adds 'the boys who ride the horses…do runne races for wagers, with a desire for praise or hope of victorie'. Twenty-five years later, Richard the Lionheart gave a purse of gold for the winner of a three-mile (4.8 km) race in London. Although the first race of which accurate details were recorded took place in 1377 between horses belonging to the Earl of Arundel and the Prince of Wales, monarchs since the time of King Stephen (reigned 1135–1154) had imported 'hot-blooded' horses for racing. These were often described as 'Arabs', but Syria, Turkey, Persia and parts of North Africa were all considered 'Arab' countries and the term was used indiscriminately in the description of horses. However, Queen Elizabeth I's racing stable at Greenwich was said to contain forty Arabs, Barbs and Turks and Thomas Blundeville, writing in 1558 of the horse breeds then known in Britain, begins with, 'The Turk because he cometh the farthest', describing them as 'very swift in their running and of great courage'. He goes on to state that: 'All the horses which come from any of the Turkes' domains or the frontiers of his nearest neighbours be called Turkey horses', which is of interest as Blundeville never mentions Arab horses in his list. Moreover, because the Turkish Empire covered much of Arabia and Syria, and Turkey itself controlled the Mediterranean coastline, it forbade these other areas from making contact with the West, so it is highly probable that genuinely Arab horses could have been imported under the name of Turkish horses.

Despite the campaigning of a zealous and outspoken critic of racing called Hinde (who blamed it 'as the cause of profanity, cursing, brawling, quarrelling, bad example and idleness') the sport progressed through Stuart times as James I was a keen patron. In fact, he paid £500 for an Arab stallion, known as the Markham Arabian after the London merchant of that name who originally bought it in Constantinople, but it failed miserably both on the racecourse and as a sire, and his second Arab stallion fared little better. However, undaunted, James did much to promote racing. He even organized an impromptu race meeting on ice when the River Ouse froze over in 1605, the horses presumably being shod with 'sharps' set into their shoes. The king, who stated that 'the mere sight of great horses bored him to tears owing to their clumsy appearance' also founded a royal stud chiefly composed of Arabians and oriental mares, and established public race meetings, especially at Newmarket. Even pony races were popular, especially in parts of Scotland, one notable race run on Solway Sands being won by Lord Hamilton's pony, and private wagers and matches became a regular feature of many public gatherings.

The Civil War, which cost Charles I his head, severely disrupted the breeding of racehorses as racing was curtailed under Cromwell who, although a keen sportsman himself, bowed to pressure from his advisers and banned the sport for part of 1654 and again in 1659 because it was believed that race meetings could have been used for Royalist uprisings. Nevertheless, it was said that one of Cromwell's few extravagances was the importation of splendid horses – Barbs from Tripoli and Arabs from Aleppo – with the result that there were better stables under Cromwell than under the former King. Sir Charles Fenwick, Stud Master to Charles I, had his own renowned racing stud confiscated by the Parliamentarians, who similarly claimed other studs, including the late King's, valued at £1,982, which was put up for sale. Six of the best horses from the latter were bought by the Duke of Ormonde and taken to Ireland to improve the local stock, which they did, but not for the breeding of racehorses.

With the coming of the Restoration and Charles II on the throne, racing once more flourished and many consider Charles II to have been the founder of the prosperous bloodstock industry of today. He was very influential in the development of Newmarket as a racing centre, and he certainly appreciated good horses – after his escape following the Battle of Worcester and with a £1,000 ransom on his head, he had been forced to ride a mill horse which he described as 'the heaviest dull jade' when blistered royal feet had prevented him from walking. Despite opposition from the Church, races began to take place all over Britain at fairs and on holidays, and greater attention was now paid to the breeding of racehorses. Berenger, writing of this period, said: 'Public races were now established, and such horses as had given proof of superior abilities became famous and their breed was cultivated.' The small size of early racehorses probably indicates some native pony blood far back, and at one time it was estimated that the average height of racehorses increased 1 in (2.54 cm) every twenty-five years, a claim supported by W. J. Gordon, author of *The Horse World of London*, published in 1893, who wrote: 'The Thoroughbred racehorse increases a hand in height every century; in 1700 he stood 13.2, he now stands 15.2.'

As the breeding of racehorses began to escalate into something of a science, the number of Arab, Barb, Turk and other Eastern imports increased and between 1803 and 1814 alone it is recorded that 84 Arabians, 47 Barbs, 32 Turks and 4 Persian horses were imported into England. By putting selected stallions to the best mares available (which included both imported and English mares, some originating in Yorkshire but at least one allegedly out of an Irish Hobby), the English Thoroughbred was developed in the eighteenth century into the ultimate racehorse. Jack Fairfax-Blakeborough, the equine historian who lived in Yorkshire, believed that: 'Every Thoroughbred in the world is descended from seventy-eight foundation mares and three Eastern imported stallions, and of these seventy-eight original mares, over seventy were Yorkshire racing Galloways located in North Yorkshire.' Their geographical location notwithstanding, these mares were probably of imported origin, and in his *Northern Turf*

History, Fairfax-Blakeborough clarified the definition of 'Galloway' in respect to the breeding of racehorses when he wrote: 'The term Galloway then (as it continues to be in Yorkshire today) referred rather to the size than the origins of the animals, and it is very doubtful if the ponies had any connection with the Scottish breed… Officially, a Galloway was a horse of 14 hands or under.'

Of all the British breeds, the Thoroughbred has benefited from having the most accurate records kept of its bloodlines, thanks primarily to James Weatherby, who was appointed as Secretary of the Jockey Club in 1770. An able and entrepreneurial man, he was responsible for publishing the first racing calendar in 1773, which listed all the races for the year, and he also collated information on all the contestants and their performances. In the light of this, from 1751 onward, a system of weight variations was introduced, which enabled horses of different ages to compete against each other, carrying weights appropriate to their age. From this early 'weight for age' system (which continues in essence today), the more complex system of handicapping developed, by which horses are (subject to certain constraints) allotted weight on the basis of their perceived ability, rather than simply their age. James Weatherby was also responsible for promoting in 1793 the publication of the first *General Stud Book*, which constituted a definitive record of the 400 horses accepted as being the foundation stock for the Thoroughbred. As such, every Thoroughbred alive today can be traced back to the first volume of this book. Now published every four years, the *General Stud Book* records all Thoroughbred matings and births in Great Britain and Ireland. Considering that the total registrations for 2007 numbered 18,472, of which over 68% were foaled in Ireland, it is a stark contrast to the UK registration numbers for the Suffolk Punch, which average 30 per annum.

In a lengthy treatise dated 1644, General Lord Fairfax boldly claimed that all British breeds, large and small, were of foreign origin, but with patchy and incomplete records to work from, some element of speculation is inevitable. Sir Alfred Pease, who undertook extensive research into the origins of the horses of Yorkshire, concluded: 'If you could extend completely a pedigree back to the 20th generation, you would in that generation alone have to write down the names of 1,048,576 stallions and mares', adding: 'the further you go back the less perfect the record'. So much foreign blood has been imported into Britain and so many crosses tried that, according to a writer of 1727, 'The true bred English horse hardly exists, unless we may account the horses to be such that are bred wild in some of our forests and among the mountains.'

Chapter 5

THE BRITISH
HORSE BREEDS

*Whereas the Thoroughbred is a symbol of wealth,
the heavy horse is a token of the life
and work of ordinary people.*
SHIRE HORSE SOCIETY REPORT, 1988

HEAVY DRAUGHT BREEDS

The Development of Heavy Draught Horses

The British Isles are home to three distinct breeds of heavy draught horse, all of which owe their origins to Norman imports – although much additional blood has been introduced since that time and refined through selective breeding to produce what are arguably the finest breeds of their type in the world. Their fortunes since medieval times have been a cycle of decline and revival and, as with all breeds, it has been their ability to adapt to changing demands that has ensured their survival to the present day. When warfare no longer needed heavy horses, a new market for these immensely strong and active horses emerged in agriculture, where faster and more thorough cultivation of the land ousted the slow and outdated work oxen, and the value of a good cart horse tripled during the twelfth century to eighteen shillings. Hollinshead, writing in 1587, stated: 'Our cart or plough horses are commonly so strong that fifty foot of timber, forty bushels of salt or four quarters of wheat is considered a normal load', adding that agricultural horses of the time could easily carry 4 cwt (32 st, or 203 kg). There are records dating from that period through to the eighteenth century of horses harnessed to waggons full of sand with the wheels partly sunk into the ground to increase the strain, and even of horses harnessed to living trees, to test their strength. Less extreme pulling matches were common up until comparatively recent times, highlighting the emphasis put on the strength of these breeds as their most esteemed quality. As better roads came into being, heavy horses found ready employment moving cargoes of immense weight in cities, on docks and on the roads, and the breeds prospered as Britain's agriculture and commerce boomed.

The Shire

Sir Walter Gilbey, an authority on British horse breeds, contended that the Shire was the purest survivor of the 'great horse' of England. With so much emphasis put on size and strength alone, it is evident that the imports from the Low Countries often had little finesse, and one writer described the Black Fen Horses as ugly, gross and sluggish. Known by some as the *snail breed* on account of their slowness, other writers were more charitable and described them as active trotters despite their coarseness. Thomas Blundeville, writing in 1558, said that the farm horses of his native Norfolk should be: 'Of a high stature, strongly made, large and faire, and have a trotting pase…for it is not meet for divers respects that horses for service should amble.' From the rather ponderous farm horse of the Eastern counties, known as the Norfolk Farm Horse, Lincolnshire Black, Black Fen Horse and by a number of other names all referring to the same type, the Shire was selectively bred and developed into the substantial but high-quality animal we know today. One theory is that Eastern blood was introduced to the breed to counterbalance the coarse heads, heavily feathered legs and drooping quarters, but a more certain beneficial influence was the work of Robert Bakewell (1725–1795), the celebrated cattle and sheep breeder, who turned his attention to farm horses with great success. Bakewell's policy was to inbreed in order to establish the desired characteristics, but his work took some time to achieve its goals. William Marshall, writing in 1788, four years after he had praised one of Bakewell's stallions, was very disparaging of the early progenitors of the Shire horse, commenting: 'The breed of grey rats with which this island has of late been overrun is not a greater pest than this breed of black Fen horses.'

Bakewell was rather secretive about how he improved the early Shire, known at one time as the Bakewell Black, but it has been theorized that he may have introduced Norfolk Trotter blood (itself a descendant of the Black Fen Horse), to bring an element of quality and activity while not losing any of the size and strength that was deemed so important. It is believed that he also used selected Friesian horses, from stock brought to the area by Dutch drainage experts who were working in the eastern counties at that time. These horses may, in fact, have been virtually the same as the Norfolk Trotters because, by that time, the Friesian had developed from a coarse draught animal into a fast trotting road horse. Indeed, encouraged by William, Prince of Orange, trotting had become a popular sport in the Low Countries and was soon to be taken up with enthusiasm in Britain in the form of matches and road races. The 'excellent variety of well-shaped black nags', further described by John Lawrence in his *History and Delineation of the Horse,* published in 1809, as 'excellent trotters' and 'doubtless originating in Flemish stock' were in all probability Norfolk Trotters. A 1791 painting of a Bakewell Black stallion with Dishley Grange, Bakewell's Derbyshire farm, in the background portrays a very powerfully built black horse showing a lot of Friesian characteristics in the stance and head carriage.

In 1878, when a society was formed to foster the breed, it was agreed that Bakewell Black was a misnomer, partly because there were other accepted colours in the breed, and The Old English Cart Horse Society was suggested then adopted, following agreement that the word 'Old' be dropped from the title. However, Welsh, Irish and Scottish breeders subsequently objected to the word 'English' in the title and in June 1883 the name was changed to Shire Horse Society in recognition of the Midland Shires where this impressive breed was principally bred.

Although the horses bred by Bakewell and those who continued his work were certainly big, they were nowhere near the size of the modern Shire, which is now not only the largest of the British heavy horse breeds – with many examples standing up to 19 hands (193 cm) and weighing over a ton (1,016 kg) – but the largest breed of horse in the world. The record for the tallest horse belongs to Sampson (later renamed Mammoth), a Shire bred by Thomas Cleaver of Toddington Mills, Bedfordshire, and foaled in 1846, who measured 21 hands 2½ in (220 cm) as a four-year-old and

The modern-day Shire owes much to the work of Robert Bakewell,
the eighteenth-century livestock breeder, and it is now the largest breed
of horse in the world.

weighed 30 cwt (1,524 kg). At a Shire Horse Society London Show, two Shire geldings harnessed tandem fashion to a springless cart moved an 18$^{1}/_{2}$ ton (18,796 kg) load, and on the return journey the shaft horse took the whole weight, while at the British Empire Exhibition at Wembley in 1924 a Shire gelding called Vulcan, owned by Liverpool Corporation, pulled the equivalent of a dead start of 29 tons (29,464 kg). Earlier, in 1893, a pair of English Shire horses had pulled a load allegedly consisting of fifty pine logs weighing over 125 tons (127,000 kg) and stacked on a sledge for a quarter of a mile (0.4 km) over ice in Michigan, North America.

Despite their size and strength, there were some constitutional problems in the developmental years of the Shire. Pickford's, the hauliers, who employed large numbers of draught horses throughout the nineteenth century, always favoured Shire crosses as they found the hooves of pure-breds did not stand up to the road work, but rigorous veterinary examinations at the Society's London Shire Show virtually eliminated the problems of unsoundness in wind and limb which had often been associated with their Black Fen ancestors and this, together with the work the Society was doing to promote the breed, did much to expand the home market. With unsoundness issues resolved, the working life of geldings in towns and cities increased and their financial value soared and was maintained right through to the Second World War. In fact, during the bleak days of the Great Depression, the sale of Shire foals kept many farmers solvent. At one point there were over a million pure-bred Shire horses in Britain, not to mention the many thousands of part-breds working throughout the land in everything from forestry and agriculture to delivery work and heavy transport.

The forming of a registry in 1878 had also encouraged the export of Shires abroad, notably to the United States, where the American Shire Horse Association was founded in 1885 with financial support from the Shire Horse Society in Britain. For breeders, the lucrative export market was very welcome and huge numbers of Shires, mainly stallions, crossed the Atlantic, surpassing in numbers the importation to America of any other breed. One family, the Trumans of Bushnell, Illinois, imported the first Shires into the United States in 1878 and five years later, after their second shipment, John H. Truman announced to the English breeders that he believed the American market would be for registered horses and he encouraged breeders to get their horses entered in the stud book. His words created a flood of registrations as his prophecy proved accurate and the American market opened up. Between 1900 and 1918 alone the Trumans imported 1,032 Shires, and it is significant that around 25 per cent of the horses listed in the first eleven volumes of the American stud book covering 1885–1918 were imported from England. Exports to other countries also proliferated at this time.

A Shire stallion owned by the Duke of Devonshire, showing the size and muscularity developed in the breed by the turn of the twentieth century.

The Clydesdale

The need for a similar type of horsepower in Scotland as in England meant that, since Bakewell's day, many Shires, as well as draught horses from other European countries, travelled up into Scotland, with the result that the early Scottish draught horse was little different from that in England. During the eighteenth century one of the Dukes of Hamilton, a wealthy local landowner, imported what were described as 'six Flemish Great Horses', a breed which had previously been shipped regularly to Scotland, and the Duke generously made his six stallions available for covering local mares.

By the early nineteenth century, Scottish breeders were establishing their own breed of active, strong draught horse, not quite as large as the Shire, selecting as foundation stock horses from both Scotland and England which possessed the qualities they sought. The breed was developed in Lanarkshire, which at that time was known as Clydesdale, and in 1826 the breed made its debut at the Glasgow Exhibition under that name.

Just as Bakewell had greatly influenced the breeding and improvement of draught horses in England, so did Lawrence Drew, a Scotsman born in 1826, north of the border. Although they worked a century apart, Drew's ideas and abilities were remarkably similar to Bakewell's and his skills were recognized in England as well as among his fellow countrymen. He once said:

> If a horse has merit, this is, if it has all good points of a first-rate draught horse – substance, symmetry, size, weight, bone, sinew, muscle, durability and action, and if it be free from all hereditary diseases, you may depend that blood and pedigree are in that horse in a degree sufficient for the purpose of breeding first-rate stock or performing hard work.

Drew was responsible for taking many Shire horses up into Scotland and he had a profound influence on the Clydesdale horse, but he was not a supporter of separate breed registries, believing there should be only one registry for draught horses in Britain. To maintain some form of record of what he was doing personally, Drew did establish a select Clydesdale register in 1883, but it was discontinued after his death the following year. Meanwhile the Clydesdale Horse Society was formed in June 1877 and in the following year it published the first volume of its stud book.

The Clydesdale breed quickly established a reputation for strength – enabling it to pull loads of over a ton (1,016 kg) at a walking speed of 5 mph (8 kph) – as well as inherent soundness, docility and a more elevated action than most other draught breeds. With the development of the Lanarkshire coalfields and improvements to the roads, the Clydesdale prospered. At the peak of its agricultural and industrial ascendancy, Scotland had around

The Clydesdale, although neither as big nor as powerful as the Shire, has a more elevated action which contributes to its popularity in the show-ring.

140,000 farm horses in addition to the thousands of working horses in towns and cities, and most would have been pure or part-bred Clydesdales. Surprisingly, although Yorkshire had the reputation for producing the best carriage horses, according to W. J. Gordon writing in 1893: 'Of late a good many of them trace their maternal pedigree through the Clydesdale breed, the result being a gain in hardiness and in the firmness and fitness of the feet for the hard paving of the town streets'.

Like the Shire, Clydesdales were exported regularly throughout the British Commonwealth and also to America, and 1,617 Clydesdale stallions were exported to destinations around the world in 1911 alone. Between

1850 and 1945 the Clydesdale Horse Society issued export certificates for 20,183 Clydesdales to go as far afield as South America, Russia, Austria and Italy, and there are now thriving Clydesdale Societies in Australia, New Zealand, South Africa, Canada and the United States. Teams of up to sixteen Clydesdales were used in Australia at one time to pull multi-furrow ploughs, and it was mainly Clydesdales that made up the seventy-six horses once harnessed together to pull a 14-ton (14,224 kg) wool waggon out of a flooded river in Australia. A Clydesdale also established a record price in Britain for a heavy horse when the stallion, Baron of Buchlyvie, was sold at public auction for £9,500 in 1911.

The Suffolk Punch

According to Camden's *Britannia,* the Suffolk Punch can be traced back to 1506, which would make it the oldest of the British draught breeds. It certainly has the longest unbroken written pedigree of any breed and this goes back to a stallion foaled in 1768 and known as Crisp's Horse of Ufford, to which every living Suffolk can be traced. As with the Clydesdale and Shire, the progenitors of the breed were undoubtedly of continental European origin, most probably Belgian. However, the Suffolk is quite distinct from the other two heavy breeds in two respects: it is always chestnut in colour (although the shade may vary and the breed society recognizes seven shades for registration) and it is always 'clean-legged', or free from feather. This latter feature was bred into it, to make the Suffolk easy to care for when working the heavy clay soils of its native region. A painting of a Suffolk mare by the Royal Academician, James Ward, dated 1794, shows a short-backed, deep-bodied, clean-legged animal which, although no great beauty, displays many good points and is of definite Suffolk type.

Since those early days the Suffolk has been selectively bred to produce a handsome, compact horse which breeds very true to type, and there has subsequently never been any necessity to alter the breed standard, which was originally drawn up in 1919. Although, during the nineteenth century and up to the First World War, Suffolks were exported to such places as

America, Australia, Africa and Russia, these exports were mainly for cross-breeding purposes. For the most part, over the centuries, the pure breed has largely remained in the region where it originated, the reason being that East Anglia was, until comparatively recently, relatively isolated from the rest of Britain. By the 1930s, when one or two studs were being established in other parts of the country with the potential to distribute the breed more widely, it was too late as agricultural mechanization was poised to replace the working farm horse. The large, level farms of the Suffolk's home area were ideal for testing the early tractors and implements, and the traditional work horses were quickly ousted.

The deep, round-ribbed body set on short legs gave rise to the Suffolk's popular name of 'punch'. Other particular features of the Suffolk include its

The Suffolk was specifically bred to be clean-legged or free from feather to work the heavy clay soils of its native Suffolk and the surrounding counties.

Some British heavy draught breeds have found favour in continental Europe. Suffolk and Shire pairs competing in the Route du Poisson, a twenty-four hour relay race commemorating the extraordinary journeys made by draught teams carrying fresh fish between the French ports and Paris.

docile nature and longevity, a typical example being a Suffolk gelding owned by a London coal merchant, which was shown at the London Cart Horse Parade for seventeen successive years up until he was twenty-one years old. At the height of their popularity, there were huge numbers of Suffolks throughout East Anglia and the neighbouring counties, and it is estimated that before the First World War the agriculture of south-eastern England was virtually dependent on this long-established breed.

Ascendancy and Decline of Working Heavy Draught Horses
Despite predictions in Victorian times that the coming of the railways would herald the end of horsepower, this proved not to be the case as more horses than ever were required to work in town and country. When Pickford's downsized their road haulage operations between London, Manchester and Liverpool because of the opening of the Liverpool and

Birmingham railroad, their advertisement in the London Press on Tuesday June 20th 1837 for the sale of 'Twenty remarkably fine, powerful, young, fresh, good-actioned, short-legged horses' attracted much interest from 'noblemen and gentlemen, job masters, coach proprietors, tradesmen, and others working draught horses.' It was not until 1883 that the Great Western Railway acquired its own horses for the first time, having used contractors and job masters previously, and in that year they purchased 501 heavy horses for Paddington and Smithfield depots. By the 1890s the heavy horse population of Britain had reached its highest point, and at its peak Glasgow Corporation bought 4,000 Clydesdales for use in its trams in one year. Heavy draught horses pulled the brewers' drays, railway vans, carriers' waggons, vestry carts and every other type of heavy commercial vehicle in towns and cities and, as late as 1948, the railways still employed 8,793 horses in their shunting and good yards and on the road between depots. The value of strong, good quality, young draught horses was pushed even higher by the foreign buyers, whose agents regularly attended shows and cart horse parades in search of suitable purchases. As a rule, Shires were the preferred breed for the heaviest work like pulling brewers' drays for, as one late Victorian writer observed: 'Clydesdales, though now improving every year, do not run quite heavy enough for brewers' work.'

The downturn in the fortunes of the heavy draught breeds really began soon after the First World War, when tractors started replacing the traditional farm horse for all work on the land, while motor vehicles were beginning to commandeer road haulage. The need for greater agricultural output during the Second World War gave mechanization on the farms a great boost and thousands of heavy horses were sold off. Some farms in the eastern counties were reported as getting rid of up to forty horses in a single day and, with so many unwanted animals flooding the market, prices plummeted and slaughterhouses were the main buyers. In 1946, 200 Clydesdale stallions were licensed and working in England; three years later the figure had dropped to 80. The 1960s and 1970s saw breed numbers for Shires, Clydesdales and Suffolks dwindle further, 1963 being cited as the lowest point for all heavy horse breeds, and by 1975 the Clydesdale was categorized by the Rare Breeds Survival Trust (RBST) as 'vulnerable', although with an increase in numbers in recent years the future is looking more optimistic. The Suffolk fared even worse and in 1966 only nine pure-bred foals were born and the breed was heading towards extinction. Although numbers have improved thanks to the perseverance of the Suffolk Horse Society and a dedicated body of breeders, at the time of writing the breed still has RBST 'critical' classification. However, in recent years the heavy breeds have all enjoyed some resurgence of interest.

LIGHT DRAUGHT BREEDS

The Irish Draught

While the Shire, Clydesdale and Suffolk Punch fully met the needs of agriculture in mainland Britain, the Irish farmers needed and bred a lighter, more adaptable stamp of horse which was as suitable for work in harness or under saddle as on the land. 'Irish Draught' was a generic term coined by the English horse dealers and army requisitioning officers who, along with buyers from many other countries had, for centuries, travelled to Ireland to purchase horses, and the name referred to the substantial stamp of animal from which the world-famous Irish hunter was bred. The Irish Draught was produced from the indigenous horses of Ireland, in reality ponies of up to around 14 hands (142 cm), mixed with the blood of larger, heavier horses, first introduced following the English invasion of Ireland in 1172.

There is evidence to suggest that many of the early Irish Draught type originated in Galway and the Connemara region and grew larger and stronger on the better land in less rugged parts of Ireland. At the end of the eighteenth century, heavy horses from England were introduced to give additional strength and size, but these had heavily feathered legs which did not find favour with the Irish farmers and breeders, who selected the heavier of their own horses to eventually produce a type of light draught horse of consistent stamp. Unlike many breeds with identifiable foundation sires, meticulously kept breeding records, well-known and influential studs, or pioneering patrons, the Irish Draught simply developed to suit the environment and the needs of those who bred and worked them and it remained a *type* for several centuries.

In 1887 the Irish Government initiated an annual grant of £5,000 to encourage the improvement of livestock, of which £3,200 was allocated to horse-breeding, the Royal Dublin Society being initially entrusted with the administration of the grant. With the establishment of the Department of Agriculture in 1900, responsibility for administering financial aid to encourage improvements in horse-breeding was transferred to the new department and, whilst Thoroughbred stallions were mainly used up until 1907 in order to promote the production of hunters, after that date Irish Draught stallions began to feature more and more as it was felt that stronger types were needed for tillage purposes in many parts of the country. In 1901 a stud book was proposed, but it was not until three years later that the Department of Agriculture introduced a premium scheme for stallions, thirteen of which were granted premiums. Seven years later, the Department received grant aid to set up a register of mares with the aim of sending them to the approved stallions and 264 mares and 18 stallions were inspected and approved as being of true Irish Draught type, but the logistics of getting the mares to the stallions caused the scheme to fail. In 1917 the Department of Agriculture decided to make a concerted effort to revive the breeding of the native draught horse of Ireland and, despite the thousands shipped off to mainland Europe for military service, they introduced an inspection scheme which passed 374 of the 1,800 mares put forward and 44 of the 270 stallions. The three inspectors for the scheme produced a report which concluded: 'We are confident that the success of the scheme is assured, and that in time there will be in the country a distinct breed of clean-legged draught horses, which could not be excelled, and in sufficient numbers to supply the demand now existing for a heavier class of sire.'

Regarding sales for military and other purposes, a thriving trade in

Irish horses, the bulk of which were of Irish Draught type, had long been established when W. J. Gordon, writing of London in 1893, noted: 'Our cab horses are generally Irish, many of them being shipped from Waterford', and it was estimated that at the time there were around 15,000 cab horses in London alone. Military use constituted a ready market for many more and as the same writer reported: 'When a military horse is "cast" [retired from active service], and all military horses are "cast" at fourteen years old, a requisition for a substitute goes to the Remount Depot at Woolwich, and the substitute arrives a day or two later from the Emerald Isle, generally shipped direct by Daly or some other Dublin dealer.' He added that the trooper and his complete kit could weigh up to 23 st (146 kg) which he considered 'heavy enough for the class of horse which has nothing of the "dray" type about it.'

The First World War engendered an insatiable demand for 'a cart horse that could trot, eat less, endure more, and be placid and fast enough for artillery', and which also needed to be clean-legged, and the Irish Draught suited the purpose well, proving its worth drawing the gun carriages and supply waggons in the deep Flanders mud. Captain C. D. Evans, who commanded the Ballsbridge Remount Depot, the largest in Ireland during the First World War, spoke highly of the Irish Draught horses which passed through his hands, a view confirmed by the War Office reports summarizing the merits of the various breeds and types employed at the front during the Great War. The heavy draught breeds were reported to be slow and delicate and to lack stamina, as well as being expensive to feed, while the horses bred in the south of Ireland and primarily from Irish Draught mares met favour from the buyers of artillery horses. It was reported that some Irish Draught horses left Kilkenny in 1914 to work in the gun teams and were still there to march into Brussels in 1918 in the Ceremonial Parade, and at one time the Belgian Army was horsed entirely with Irish-bred horses, the bulk of them Irish Draughts, which were shipped direct from Ireland.

Helped by government grants, the breed survived and numbers grew

Brian and Liz Gates' Irish Draught ride-and-drive mare, Monnybrook Amanda.

until the 1950s when tractors displaced the working farm horse in Ireland as they had in the rest of the British Isles, and the breed went into inevitable decline. Fortunately, the recognition of the value of the Irish Draught as foundation stock for breeding not only hunters but show-jumpers and eventers brought about a revival in its fortunes. In 1967 the Dublin Horse Show reintroduced Irish Draught classes after a lapse of forty-two years, and in 1976 the Irish Draught Horse Society was founded. The modern Irish Draught is a powerful, deep-bodied horse with substance and quality and, as the fashion for continental Warmbloods has levelled out, the pure-bred Irish Draught has shown itself to be a versatile performer in a wide range of disciplines and is enjoying increasingly widespread popularity.

The Cleveland Bay and Yorkshire Coach Horse

As with the Irish Draught, the Cleveland Bay is, in some respects, also a light draught breed, developed in this case in the area of North Yorkshire from which it takes its name. It derives from a clean-legged race of usually bay horses dating back to late medieval times and later known as Chapman horses which, as explained in the previous chapter, were used extensively as pack horses by the abbeys and monastic houses who bred them in large numbers. After the dissolution of the monasteries in 1539 these horses were used for farm work and for transporting minerals, principally iron ore, from the mines to the smelting works and coastal ports. It was quite usual for these strong, short-legged horses to carry up to 600 lb (273 kg) of iron ore in baskets strapped to their backs, while other cargo included farm produce, salted fish from ports like Whitby, wool, potash, charcoal, alum, lime from the southern escarpment overlooking the Plain of York and coal which was used in the furnaces where the lime was burnt. During the seventeenth century, the Chapman horse developed into the Cleveland Bay when an infusion of Andalusian and Barb blood was introduced into the breed by the wealthy landowning families among whom the monastic estates had been shared out following the dissolution a century earlier, and whose travels abroad had resulted in an influx of Arab and Barb horses. During the Civil War of the 1640s, aspiring military leaders who could afford it equipped themselves with an Andalusian stallion as a charger, which set them apart from the troopers who rode geldings – a throwback to medieval times. Those who prudently backed the victorious side kept their redundant warhorses and used them for breeding instead, and Lord Fairfax, who was given the Helmsley Estate in lieu of unpaid wages, found himself in possession of the Spanish horses that the Duke of Buckingham had brought north. This situation resulted in large numbers of Andalusian stallions becoming available to owners of Chapman horses, and from these sustained crossings the Cleveland Bay emerged as a distinct breed during the eighteenth century.

Cleveland Bay breeders always declared that their horses were 'free from taint of black or blood', but while it has been asserted that there was no evidence of the coarse farm horses of Lincolnshire and the surrounding area in the Cleveland pedigrees, some oriental blood was introduced in the early eighteenth century. Bearing in mind that racing in those days often meant 4-mile (6.4 km) heats carrying far greater weights than is the case today, the racehorses of that time must have had considerable stamina, which they passed on to their Yorkshire descendants. Sir Alfred Pease, a staunch supporter of the breed in late Victorian times, wrote that every Cleveland Bay in the stud book could be traced to eighteenth-century racing sires, although these were probably the 'Yorkshire Galloways' often referred to in old documents, rather than the modern Thoroughbred as we know it today, and the blood was primarily passed down through the distaff side. One particular horse known to have great influence was Jalap, an ex-racehorse foaled in 1758 whose sire, Regulus, was by the Godolphin Arabian (who, despite his name, was actually a Barb.) William Marshall, writing in 1788, said the improvement in the horses of Yorkshire over the preceding two decades 'was principally effected by one horse, Jalap, a full-bred horse whose pedigree and performance are well known upon the turf'. Interestingly, Jalap's stud fee was five guineas for blood horses and two guineas for Chapman mares. Another stallion, Manica, foaled in 1707 and a son of the Darley Arabian, can also be found in many Cleveland Bay pedigrees. Hindson's Sportsman, a typical Cleveland Bay of 1876, had forty-six crosses of Manica in his pedigree.

With improvements made to roads and the subsequent proliferation of wheeled vehicles for every type of transport, the Cleveland Bay became immensely popular in the nineteenth century, when the Yorkshire horse dealers bought huge numbers of them at horse fairs like Boroughbridge, Howden and York and sold them on to the new coaching proprietors for around £25 each. Although the horses were only meant to work one 10-mile (16 km) stage per day with the fourth day off, many worked more and the turnover in unsound or worked-out horses was considerable. On one route alone in 1821, twenty horses dropped dead from overwork, although it was always said that the Cleveland Bay took work better than most.

Because of their uniform colour they were easier than many other breeds to put together as matched pairs and teams, and many Cleveland Bays travelled south from their native Yorkshire to draw the elegant carriages of London's fashionable and wealthy. At one point a 'Yorkshire pair' was considered quite a status symbol among the socially pretentious Victorians and, as the number of private carriages in the country rose from 60,000 in 1814 to 250,000 by 1860 and 500,000 by 1901, Cleveland Bays soared in popularity. In London alone, 300,000 horses of all types were employed by the end of the nineteenth century, and that was less than 10 per cent of the total horse population of England. The demand was so great that between 1862 and 1882 imports of foreign-bred carriage horses increased six-fold and, although most people acknowledged that none had anything like the stamina of the English breeds, in 1876 a total of 40,700 horses were imported into Britain.

By the end of the nineteenth century, the demand for a lighter and faster stamp of carriage horse resulted in many Cleveland Bays being

Peter Dallow and Linda Skeat's team of pure-bred Cleveland Bays driven by Charles Matheson.

crossed with Thoroughbreds to produce the 'New Cleveland Bay' or 'Yorkshire Coach Horse' as it was better known, threatening the old breed with extinction. One strain with a high percentage of Thoroughbred blood was known as the Howdenshire Cleveland, its name derived from the Howden Horse Fair held every September where so many of these horses were sold. Writing of the Yorkshire Coach Horse, which he believed to be 'the most beautiful breed of coach horse the world has ever seen', Sir Alfred Pease said: 'During the height of the London season hundreds of pairs of these magnificent animals might be seen in Hyde Park every afternoon.' Until 1884 they were included, by the public at least, in the general term 'Cleveland Bays'. This date is significant: it was in 1884 at a meeting in the Black Lion Hotel, Stockton-on-Tees, that the Cleveland Bay Horse Society was founded to encourage farmers, who were the principle breeders, to maintain their pure-bred stock, and a retrospective stud book, published in the same year, contained the details of 560 horses dating back to the late eighteenth century. Sir Alfred Pease was among the body of men who drew up the Cleveland Bay Horse Society's first official statement: 'We assert without fear of contradiction that the old type of Cleveland Bay is the best and most economical animal on a farm; that it will do more work in any given period of time; consume less food, wear less shoe iron in either slow or fast work on the farm or on the road, than any other breed.'

The Cleveland Bay had the advantage over the Shire and Clydesdale of being clean-legged, and was also an ideal sort to carry a British trooper or take his turn in the field and horse artillery during the Boer War. Not only did the government remount officers buy up large numbers of Cleveland Bays; their employers handed out premiums for Cleveland Bay stallions to ensure a ready supply for future hostilities. Tales of the Cleveland Bay's versatility and prowess are legion. One horse belonging to a farmer called Arthur Bell was being worked in a plough when the hunt came past in full cry and the horse leapt out of the furrow to follow the chase, plough and all. The owner, sportingly, loosed the traces, mounted the horse and stayed with the hounds right to the kill, where he was presented with the fox's brush in recognition of their performance. Star, a pure-bred mare, was the top high-jumper of her day in 1863, and another extraordinary horse with Cleveland ancestry on the distaff side was Peter Simple, who came third in the Grand National in 1841, 1842 and 1845 and won several less prestigious steeplechases. It is also interesting that the oldest recorded horse in Britain, Old Billy, who was foaled in 1760 and lived to the remarkable age of sixty-two, having worked as a barge horse for the Mersey and Irwell Navigation Company for most of his life, was said to be 'a Cleveland Bay with Eastern blood'.

Despite the popularity of the Yorkshire Coach Horse, the purist Cleveland Bay breeders were adamantly against allowing coach horse blood into the old breed and when King George V, who kept a stud of Yorkshire Coach Horses, offered his prize-winning stallion, Tantalus, to the Cleveland Bay Society in 1921, it caused ructions within the Society. Some members felt they could not look the royal gift horse in the mouth and were obliged to accept the King's offer, while others resigned in disgust, referring to the well-intentioned monarch as 'Defender of the Faith but not of the Cleveland Bay'. (There had, in fact, been a similar conflict back in 1888 when a group of members had tried unsuccessfully to get a coach horse into the stud book and resigned to form the Yorkshire Coach Horse Society.)

Like the other draught breeds, the Cleveland Bay hit a low point in the 1950/60s when tractors replaced horses as the motive power on farms, causing one equestrian writer to say of the breed: 'Though he is still bred for farm use, and good Cleveland Bays are kept in the Royal stables, it is probable that his days are numbered.' Fortunately, the writer was wrong. One of the breed's greatest assets, and one that has helped ensure its survival, is its pre-potency when crossed with other breeds, particularly those smaller and lighter than itself, to pass on its size, substance, hardiness, soundness and bone. For this reason, since the early nineteenth century, large numbers of Cleveland Bays have been exported to countries such as America, Canada, Australia, New Zealand and latterly Japan and Pakistan. These exports prompted one early member of the Cleveland Bay Society to lament: 'the great injury foreigners

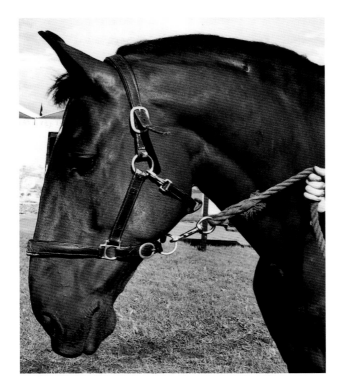

The convex profile to the head of some Cleveland Bays can be attributed to Andalusian or Barb blood in their ancestry.

have done to the breed of horses in taking away the old breed of Chapman, or as they have latterly been called, Cleveland Bays.' This writer, also, was wrong, since the success of the breed for crossing to produce show-jumpers and eventers both in Britain and elsewhere has led to an increased demand for pure-bred stock and brought about an upturn in breeding numbers in recent years, with 60–70 foals now registered annually worldwide. Some of these are born abroad; America in particular has a thriving breed society.

The typical Cleveland Bay is always bay with black points, 'red' legs being considered a sign of recent Thoroughbred blood, and the head often has a convex profile, a characteristic inherited from its Andalusian and Barb ancestry. The hooves are hard and resilient, a legacy from pack train days when the ancestors of these horses travelled hundreds of miles on stone causeways or moorland tracks unshod.

THE HACKNEY

At the height of its popularity, the Hackney horse was as influential and famous as the English Thoroughbred, both in Europe and further afield and, as Sir Walter Gilbey wrote in 1898: 'In the Hackney, we have shape, action, courage, manners, staying power and soundness. What would you more?' The Hackney originated in the late seventeenth and early eighteenth centuries from the Norfolk Roadster and Yorkshire Trotter, two not dissimilar types of all-round utility horse which developed separately but simultaneously in two of the country's principal horse-breeding areas. Renowned for their legendary stamina and ability to trot long distances at speed, these strong and active horses were equally at home taking the farmer to market as working on the farm or enjoying a day's hunting. Their stride at that time was low and ground-covering, with no exaggerated knee and hock action. In the early eighteenth century, breeders began to cross the native Hackney with imported Arab stallions, which brought some refinement to the breed without any loss of the inherent original character-istics upon which their fame was founded, and the Darley Arabian, one of the pillars of the *General Stud Book*, is attributed with considerable influence on the breed. The popularity of trotting matches increased, and newspapers dating back to the late eighteenth century abounded with reports of the trotting feats, some for private wagers, of such horses as Nonpareil, who was driven 100 miles (160 km) in nine hours, fifty-six minutes and fifty-seven seconds, or the celebrated mare, Phenomenon, who trotted 17 miles (27 km) in fifty-six minutes in 1800.

As horse-drawn vehicles developed from the rough unsprung carts of earlier times into the sophisticated carriages of Regency times, the demand for a showy carriage horse with a high head carriage and more flamboyant action started to emerge and, by the end of the nineteenth century, the craze for showing harness horses and especially high-steppers saw the Hackney breed undergo a sort of metamorphosis. The old roadster type, outdated by the whims of fashion and the advent of the motor car, was gradually

Brookeborough Flash Jack, owned by Mr. and Mrs. Brian Turner and driven by
Georgina Turner to win the 2007 Hackney Horse of the Year Championship.

replaced by the spectacular show harness animal with the ebullient action
we know today. By adapting from a strictly utilitarian animal to one
produced primarily for the show ring, the Hackney probably saved itself
from extinction, but changed considerably in the process.

The Hackney Horse Society was formed in 1883 and six months later
had attracted around 300 members and boasted The Prince of Wales,
later Edward VII, as its patron. Since the early nineteenth century,
Hackney horses had been exported to parts of the world as diverse as
Russia, India and Argentina to improve and upgrade the indigenous
stock. This movement of stock was so prevalent that, in 1873, the House
of Lords formed a select committee to review the export trade in horses,
which numbered 34,536 in 1897, many of them Hackney or Hackney
crosses.

THE THOROUGHBRED

The English Thoroughbred is probably the best-known and most widely distributed breed in the modern world. Although racing and the selective breeding of 'running horses' dates back many centuries, it was not until the late seventeenth and early eighteenth centuries that three very influential stallions were imported into England which were to become the foundation sires of the Thoroughbred: the Byerley Turk, the Darley Arabian and the Godolphin Arabian.

The Byerley Turk, who was imported into England in 1689, was believed to be of Turkmenian descent, hence his name, and he was probably an Akhal-Teke, a breed dating back to the eighth century AD and renowned throughout Asia. Legend has it that he was captured from the Turks by a Dutch officer at the Siege of Vienna in 1689 and sold to Captain Byerley, although a conflicting story tells how Captain Byerley captured the horse at Buda in the 1680s and later rode him at the Battle of the Boyne. What is certain is that the horse stood at stud in County Durham, the location of the Dragoon Guards' home barracks, and later in Yorkshire where Captain Byerley had a private stud farm. At the latter venue, the horse established a bloodline that can be traced down to important twentieth-century racehorses like The Tetrarch, a stallion never defeated on the racecourse. Another descendant of the Byerley Turk, Herod, became one of the most important sires in Thoroughbred history, with progeny winning over 1,000 races.

The Darley Arabian was brought to England in 1704 as a four-year-old following his purchase by Thomas Darley of York three years earlier, when he had been the English Consul at Aleppo in Syria. The young horse was known to be of the Maneghi bloodline, a strain specifically bred for racing, and some say that he was bought at the Aleppo horse market although others believe he was bought direct from a local sheik who later tried to renege on the deal. Legend says the sheik even sent a communication to Queen Anne claiming that: 'His incomparable stallion had been foully stolen by one of her subjects', but to no avail. The Darley Arabian stood at stud in Yorkshire and, although his services were not made available to all, he nevertheless had monumental influence by siring Flying Childers, the first outstanding racehorse, whose full brother, Bartlett's Childers, sired Squirt, who in turn sired Marske, who was the father of Eclipse, one of the greatest racehorses of all time.

The Godolphin Arabian, believed by some to have been a Barb horse from Morocco (although he was entered in his owner's personal stud books throughout as an Arab), had a chequered early history if the stories about him are true. He was allegedly sent to France from Morocco as a gift to Louis XIV but was somehow reduced to pulling a water-cart in Paris, from whence he was rescued around 1730 by Edward Coke and used as a teaser for the stallion, Hobgoblin. His potential was supposedly realized when Hobgoblin would not cover a mare, Roxana, and the teaser obliged and sired Lath, one of the most celebrated racehorses of his day. Other progeny included Cade, the sire of Matchem, and Regulus, the maternal grandsire of Eclipse. The story about the Godolphin Arabian is, however, riddled with anomalies – although it is certain that he did stand at Lord Godolphin's stud (at which time he acquired the name by which he is now known) and, whilst he did not cover vast numbers of mares, he did have a profound influence on the breed. Although the bay-brown stallion stood only 15 hands (152.5 cm) high, he was considered to be 'an usually large Eastern sire', and of the one in seven successful racehorses of the mid-eighteenth century who stood 15 hands (152.5 cm) or higher, over half were by the Godolphin Arabian or his sons.

The influence of the three main progenitors of the Thoroughbred cannot be underestimated and, as an example, in the extended pedigree of Bahram, winner of the 2,000 Guineas, Derby and St. Leger, the Darley Arabian appears 44,079 times, the Godolphin Arabian 28,232 times, and the Byerley Turk 64,032 times.

As important as the main foundation sires were in establishing the breed, there were also a number of other stallions who played significant roles in the early years but whose names were not as famous and whose influence was not so profound. The mares these stallions covered in order to produce the Thoroughbred were often described as 'English' mares and as Sir Richard Glyn, writing in 1971, commented:

> There is very strong evidence to show that there was a distinct breed of race horses in this country before the importation of Eastern sires began and from which some of the foundation mares originate. Without this stock it would not have been possible to develop the Thoroughbred in the short space of two hundred years.

Some evidence of pony blood can be found in the Thoroughbred including Zoedone, who won the Grand National in 1883 and finished second and fourth on other occasions, never falling in the race, who could be traced back thirteen generations to an Exmoor pony. Although other pony breeds including the Welsh claim to have had a role in the early ancestry of the blood horse, some equine historians believed an element of coarser blood could also be traced. One writer stated: 'We are still striving to rid ourselves of the common and cart blood, every drop of which acts as a clog on the speed which it is our object to increase'. It still remains highly likely that most of the foundation mares for the Thoroughbred were imported, and the references to the 'forty Royal mares' on the distaff side of the Thoroughbred were probably but a small number of the Iberian and Oriental horses on British soil at that time, some being located in Yorkshire. After the middle of the seventeenth century, the old term 'running horses' was replaced with 'breed' or 'bred' horses and by 1700 the term 'Thoroughbred' had come into common usage.

It would be easy to conclude that the Thoroughbred, produced specifically for the turf and guaranteed security as a breed through the international popularity of horse racing, has never historically excelled in other fields. However, evidence shows that many early blood horses used in the development of the Hackney were either celebrated trotters themselves or they became famous because their progeny were fast road horses. Jalap, a stallion whose pedigree could be traced back to the Oxford Arabian, and whose successful racing career came to an abrupt end when he broke down at a race meeting at York in the late 1760s, sired many notable trotting horses, one son being named Trotting Jalap for obvious reasons. Another Yorkshire-based Thoroughbred stallion was President, whose son, Bay President, won a class for the 'best stallion for hunters' at Northallerton in 1840 and, fifteen years later, at the age of twenty-two, won a class at Malton for the best roadster stallion. In the mid-eighteenth century, the Duke of Queensberry had shown that the early Thoroughbreds were capable of exceptional trotting speeds when he harnessed four racehorses to a light four-wheeled carriage and covered 19 miles (30.5 km) in 53 minutes 27 seconds, 4 miles an hour (6.4 kmph) faster than the first passenger train achieved in 1830 when it ran between Liverpool and Manchester. The Duke's actions did not pass unnoticed and hundreds of rejects from the turf ended their days harnessed to coaches on some of the faster stages, where their working lives was estimated to be around four years. For example, the dam of Abd-El-Kader, who won the Grand National in both 1850 and 1851, had pulled the Salisbury mail coach before being rescued to be a brood mare. Other eminent racehorses experienced even more demeaning periods as draught animals: Roquefort, winner of the 1885 Grand National, had once worked between the shafts of a dogcart and Rubio, the 1908 winner, had broken down in training so badly that he was demoted to pulling a hotel bus meeting trains until he was fit enough to go back into training. Lottery, the winner of the first Grand National in 1839, was retired from racing at the age of sixteen to spend the remainder of his working life as a plough horse.

Despite the temperamental characteristics often ascribed to the breed, many Thoroughbreds made outstanding chargers in warfare, including Copenhagen, a chestnut son of Eclipse, ridden by the Duke of Wellington throughout the Battle of Waterloo in 1815. Despite being ridden from 6.00 am to 9.00 pm, when the Duke dismounted at the end of the day the stallion still had sufficient energy left to lash out at him. Copenhagen was retired to the Duke of Wellington's estate where he was buried with full military honours in 1836.

The English
Thoroughbred
cannot be
matched by
another breed
for speed and
has dominated
racing for the
last 300 years.

The English Thoroughbred cannot be matched by any other breed for speed and distance combined (although for endurance alone, the Arab would excel) and it has dominated racing for the last 300 years as well as demonstrating its capabilities at the highest level in other competitive equestrian sports, ranging from show-jumping to polo, and many top-class show horses carry a high percentage of Thoroughbred blood or are 'clean-bred'. Partly because of its global distribution and partly because of its proven influence in upgrading other breeds (a characteristic shared only by the Arab), a surprising number of the world's breeds can trace some element of Thoroughbred blood in their pedigrees. Perhaps because the breed was developed primarily with speed in mind, there is some evidence to suggest that, without careful selection and infusions of new blood from within the breed, there is a tendency for degeneration and Thoroughbred 'weeds' are not uncommon. However, at its best the Thoroughbred is not only a horse of outstanding beauty and speed but it is arguably the finest horse in the world.

Chapter 6

THE BRITISH
PONY BREEDS

*There is hardly a branch of usefulness
for which a pony is not adapted.*
WILLIAM SCARTH DIXON, 1919

The British Isles are unique in that they are home to nine distinct and recognizable breeds of native pony, plus one non-native breed and two minority breeds that meet the criteria for a breed in that they belong to a particular strain or type whose individuals reproduce their own distinct form and characteristics with sufficient consistency over successive generations to fulfil the definition for breed status.

THE SHETLAND

The smallest of the British breeds, the Shetland, is also, size for size, the strongest and certainly one of the hardiest. The Shetland Islands, which lie about a hundred miles (160 km) off the north coast of Scotland, are open to the severest Atlantic weather and, as no point is more than four miles (6.4 km) from the sea, the frequent gales come laden with salty sea spray.

No trees can survive and the only shelter available is in small valleys or on the lee side of hills where the poor quality, peaty soil can only sustain the harsher grasses, and in bad winters ponies have survived by supplementing their diet with seaweed from the shoreline. Remains of Shetland-type ponies dating back to Iron Age times have been excavated, and it is probable that the ponies which originally populated these and other islands as well as northern mainland Scotland were larger but, isolated over many centuries on the islands, the size reduced to the 42 in (106.7 cm) maximum permitted by the Shetland Pony Stud Book Society today (Shetlands being measured not in hands, but inches). A chronicler of 1568 described the ponies of Shetland as: 'No bigger than an ass, but very strong and enduring'. Apart from a possible infusion of blood brought in by Norse settlers around 1,000 years ago, the breed has remained pure and, up until the eighteenth century, very few left the islands, where they were used for farm work on the crofts, pack work – including carrying peat for burning or seaweed as fertilizer for the fields in loads of up to 170 lb (77 kg) – as well as for riding by adults. There were also reports of them being driven four abreast in small wooden ploughs, and being used to draw small carts filled with manure for the fields. The Rev. John Brand, writing in 1701, said of Shetland ponies:

> There are some, whom an able man can lift up in his arms, yet will they carry him and a woman behind him eight miles forward and as many back…if any time in winter the storm be so great that they be straightened for food, they will come down from the hills when the ebb is in the sea, and eat the sea-ware (as likewise do the sheep).

Whether or not there is an element of licence in the first phrase, these observations show great respect for the strength and hardiness of the breed.

In 1847 an Act was passed by Parliament prohibiting the employment of children in the coal mines (where they had pulled the coal tubs along the narrow and low mine workings) and three years later a Mr. Hunting of South Hetton purchased thirty Shetland ponies, which he sold to a colliery for £4 10s each. Immediately, this sparked an insatiable demand for Shetland ponies to work in the mines and at one time around 500 ponies left the islands annually to work underground. In the 1850s a mature pony could fetch a high price but the mines' buyers wanted the best and would pay for it, and so many ponies left the Shetlands that the quality of the remaining stock became a concern. In the light of this, in 1870 Lord Londonderry, a mine owner himself, established a stud on the islands of Bressay and Noss, initiating a move towards better selection of breeding stock. He and his assistants procured the best mares available and an outstanding stallion called Jack, who proved to be the cornerstone of the stud. By the time the stud was dispersed in 1899, the groundwork for improving the breed had been done and, although subsequent electrification of the mines closed the market for pit ponies, causing many breeders to give up, sufficient staunch supporters carried on to preserve

The Parlington Stud's miniature Shetland stallion, Parlington Quentin, Supreme Champion at the 2006 Shetland Pony Stud Book Society Breed Show.

the best type. In fact, the Shetland Pony Stud Book Society, which was founded in 1890 by Lord Londonderry and other mine owners interested in promoting the breed, began organizing auction sales in the islands which were a great success and broke the virtual monopoly the dealers and mine buyers had enjoyed. (The Society continues to this day, with membership standing at around 1,800.)

However, there was also a negative influence on the breed. Over the years, the crofters' right to run any ponies on the common grazing had resulted in some inferior stallions having access to the breeding mares, and to prevent this continuing the Department of Agriculture in Scotland was instrumental in introducing the Crofters Act of 1955. This Act established the Crofter's Commission, which was empowered to regulate common grazing and included the ruling that only registered and approved stallions could be run on the common grazing, the results of which were soon evident in the improved quality of the foals produced.

Shetlands are noted for their great strength and stamina, one pony carrying a 5 st (32 kg) rider from Norwich to Yarmouth and back in 1784, a distance of 45 miles (72 km), in three hours and forty-five minutes. In more recent years, a series of tests performed in Holland revealed that, proportionate to their body weight, Shetlands were capable of pulling far greater weights than representatives of the horse breeds, an attribute which has made the breed popular in harness as well as for children's riding ponies and for all types of showing. Queen Victoria used a pair of Shetlands for driving at Holyrood Palace and at Windsor Castle. They are also noted for longevity, many ponies working well into their old age. One pony started his working life in Kimbleside Pit in 1876 as a five-year-old and was employed there for twenty-two years, during which time he was never sick or sorry – although he did have two holidays, one for six weeks in 1879 and one for thirteen weeks in 1892 resulting from strikes – and in 1896 he won third prize in the pit pony class at Durham County Show. Another Shetland pony's achievements as a show-jumper earned a mention in the South African *Cape Times* in March 1952:

One of the jumpers, a pony named Moshesh, caused roars of laughter when it entered the arena and a tumult of applause when it left. About half the size of any other competing horse, it seemed ludicrous to the audience that this animal should be expected to clear any of the jumps, some of which were higher than its back.

The tiny Shetland jumped a clear round to tie for second place on that occasion, but had been witnessed jumping up to 4 ft 3 in (1.3 m) in his paddock at home.

Over the years, a thriving export market has seen Shetlands distributed to many parts of the world including the United States, Canada, and all over Europe, notably Holland.

THE HIGHLAND

In contrast to the Shetland, its near neighbour, the Highland pony is one of the largest of the native breeds, with some examples standing up to 14.2 hands (147.3 cm). Although evolving from root stock not dissimilar to the Shetland, the better quality grazing on the mainland resulted in these ponies increasing rather than decreasing in size. Also, the introduction by Norse settlers of Scandinavian horses of the same northern European blood that greatly influenced the Norwegian Fjord ponies brought increased substance. Stallions of the best French breeds sent as gifts to James IV of Scotland were also used to increase the size and weight of these ponies, and the judicious use of Arab blood added refinement and quality.

The ancestors of the modern Highland were most probably the 'Scotch nags' referred to in old documents and records, and it is claimed that Robert the Bruce rode one. From early times, there have been two distinct types within the breed, the smaller and lighter western island type, and the larger and heavier mainland type. The differences were recognized by the Royal Highland Show with separate classes for the two types until around 1948, when they were combined under the title 'Highland and Western Island ponies', before finally becoming just Highland ponies around 1970. After the Second World War, the Department of Agriculture set up the Knocknagael Stud, originally on Skye then later moved to Inverness, to improve the breed by standing approved stallions in each area for use by the crofters.

Throughout its history, the Highland has always been an all-round utility animal, much used for farm work, shepherding and general riding. The breed was also greatly favoured by sportsmen for carrying grouse panniers or deer down from the hill: the ponies' handy size made them easy to load while their strength and surefootedness made them ideal for work on hilly terrain. A Highland pony can make light work of carrying a 20 st (127 kg) stag back from a shoot. Queen Victoria was known to enjoy exploring the hills around Balmoral riding one or other of the estate's Highland ponies, and her grandson George V's favourite pony was a grey Highland called Jock, who later followed the King's coffin in the funeral procession from Sandringham to the railway station.

In the 1950s the first pony trekking centres opened in Scotland, giving

Queen Victoria regularly rode one of the estate's Highland ponies when staying at Balmoral.

summer work for the winter-employed stalking ponies while providing the Highland with an opportunity to demonstrate its suitability in a new field of activity. Highlands also excel in harness, and many make accomplished jumpers. Although pedigree records have been kept since 1896, the Highland Pony Society was not founded until 1923. More recently, the Highland has enjoyed a wider distribution, with many studs south of the border and also in France and Australia (where there are flourishing affiliated societies), and many other countries.

THE CONNEMARA

The Connemara pony is Ireland's only recognized native pony breed and it is indigenous to the western seaboard, where its ancestors roamed the rugged, mountainous region from which the breed takes its name for centuries. The natural environment ensured that only animals of the

Ireland's only native pony breed, the Connemara, has been largely influenced by Andalsian, Thoroughbred, Arab and Barb imports over the centuries.

hardiest constitution could live out all year round and survive the wet climate and the fierce storms that blast in from the Atlantic. However, although the land is very harsh, with large areas of bog and rock, and the climate very wet, the Gulf Stream helps maintain an average winter temperature of around 42°F (5.5 °C) and frosts are virtually unknown – which results in more abundant, if not necessarily better quality grazing than might be expected. There is evidence of the existence of ponies in the west of Ireland from early times and, as mentioned earlier, many historians believe that Celts, who came to this region from western Europe via France and Spain, probably introduced some of the Connemara's early forebears. The wealthy merchants of nearby Galway are known to have traded extensively with Spain and to have brought Andalusian horses as well as Barbs and Arabs to the region, where some were used on the local pony mares, and in the nineteenth century Arab imports were also used to good effect.

Whatever influence these early imports may have had on native stock, it is certain that Connemara ponies were naturally hard and resilient, as Thomas Meleady, a Dublin horse dealer, verified when giving evidence before the Royal Commission in 1897. Recalling the ponies of Connemara of the 1860s he said:

> 'When I went down there first there was a breed of ponies in it you could get up and ride them off the grass thirty miles across the mountains as I often did from Belmullet into Ballina, and they would never tire, without a feed of oats, nor did they know what the taste of oats was.'

The Congested Districts Board, established under British rule in 1891 to administer agricultural affairs in Ireland, was responsible for introducing a number of Welsh stallions for use on Connemara mares with some satisfactory results, so it is not surprising that when Professor Ewart of Edinburgh University travelled to County Galway in 1900 to prepare a report on the Connemara ponies he concluded that there were actually five types at that time. He attributed the lack of uniformity to 'breeding from all sorts and

117

conditions of mares, and being as a rule strangely indifferent as to the pedigree of the stallions'.

The Connemara Pony Breeders' Society, formed in 1923, was aware of the diversity and described the Connemara pony as:

> …varying slightly in size and character, according to the district in which they are bred, but it is generally admitted that a compact, short-legged pony about thirteen hands two inches with good shoulders and true easy movement is the most suitable type to develop…the aim of the Society is to secure, by continued selection, a breed of ponies uniform in size and shape, suitable for general utility purposes.

The following year a panel of experts was chosen to conduct inspections of stock at various centres in the region and, from the many ponies viewed, they selected seventy-five mares and six stallions considered of suitable type to be entered in the first stud book, published in 1926.

Despite its aim of establishing uniformity within the breed, the Society purchased two small Thoroughbred stallions and one part-Arab stallion, a son of Naseel who sired many famous show ponies, to improve the riding shoulders and gaits of the breed. One of the Thoroughbreds, Little Heaven, was at stud for a number of years and produced, among others, the international show-jumper, Dundrum, out of a Connemara mare. Although only 14.3 hands (150 cm) high, Dundrum won many major competitions and cleared 7 ft 2 in (2.18 m) in a puissance at Wembley.

In 1963 the Society's stud book was closed and has remained so ever since, and seventy years after the Society first set out its aims there was little change in the re-issued breed standard except that the Connemara was now described as a riding rather than a utility pony. The English Connemara Pony Society was formed in 1946 with similar rules to its parent society, and it now publishes its own stud book.

As well as being noted for their stamina, agility and intelligence, Connemara ponies are placid and kind-natured, are excellent all-round riding and driving ponies, and are renowned for being exceptional

Mrs. J. Webb's Connemara stallion, Bunowen Castle RI, a prolific champion both
in-hand and under saddle.

jumpers. In 1935, at Olympia, the twenty-two-year-old overgrown
Connemara, The Nugget, astounded the crowd by clearing a 7 ft 2 in (2.18
m) jump and, four years later, a smaller animal, the13.2 hands (137 cm)
Little Squire, won the Open Championship at Madison Square Garden
when he apparently cleared 7 feet (2.13 m). Other notable jumpers
include Stroller, the 14.1 hands (145 cm) half-bred Connemara who
became the only pony to have ever competed in an Olympic Games when,
ridden by Marion Coakes, he was won the individual silver medal at the
1968 Mexico Olympics.

Large numbers of Connemaras have been exported around the world
and, with Connemara Pony Societies established in seventeen countries, an
International Committee of Connemara Pony Societies has been formed
which meets once a year in Cliften, County Galway, to share views and
discuss issues.

THE FELL AND DALES

The early histories of the Fell and Dales ponies of northern England are much intertwined, as both breeds had their origins in the indigenous ponies of the region which, during the Roman occupation of northern England, were subject to an element of cross-breeding with horses introduced by the occupiers and their foreign mercenaries, predominantly horses from the Friesland region, whose pre-potency and characteristics can still be seen in both breeds today. There were subsequent infusions of blood from the Galloway, examples of which were ridden by the Scottish cattle drovers and reivers who regularly passed through the northern counties, and from the Welsh Cob, with many Fell and Dales carrying the blood of Comet, a Welsh Cob famed as a trotter, who stood at stud in Westmorland for several seasons. The Dales also carries a degree of Andalusian blood, examples of which were brought into north Yorkshire in the seventeenth century, as well as Yorkshire Trotter blood, which accounts for its larger size of up to 14.2 hands (147.3 cm) while the height limit for the Fell is 14 hands (142 cm).

With the advent of the Industrial Revolution, both breeds were used extensively as pack ponies carrying up to 16 st (102 kg) of iron ore, lead ore, slate, coal or other materials from the mines to the smelting works, often travelling up to 240 miles (386 km) a week. As early as the mid-eighteenth century, the writer and traveller William Cobbett wrote about the local ponies used for drawing small two-wheeled carts full of iron ore at the smelting works in North Shields. In 1792 John Byng, later to become Viscount Torrington, also rode around Britain and, in the detailed diaries of his travels, he commented on the trains of pack ponies coming down from the lead mines in Swaledale. While these ancestors of the Dales worked on the east side of the Pennines, on the western watershed its smaller cousin, the Fell, was equally in demand for pack work. At one time it was estimated that over 300 Fell ponies left the market town of Kendal every morning for destinations all over the country, carrying cargo as diverse as tanned hides, woollen stockings, potted fish, grain, live chickens, dairy produce and bolts of cloth. Fell ponies were also used for general work on hill farms, including shepherding, while the slightly larger Dales proved itself capable of undertaking all the work on upland farms where a larger horse would have been at a disadvantage. Prior to American-bred trotting horses being introduced to the north of England around 1900, pony trotting as a sport had been very popular and both Fell and Dales ponies excelled at it.

Within fourteen years of the Fell Pony Society being formed in 1918, the depression of the 1930s and mechanization threatened the breed and, at the 1932 Stallion Show, only three ponies paraded. The Secretary of the Society used to say that it was donations from King George V that saved the breed in those bleak years, although another great supporter was the children's authoress, Beatrix Potter.

The Dales, too, had a period in which it was under threat. Cross-breeding with Clydesdales to produce a larger, heavier type of horse for draught work threatened the true Dales pony and by the end of the Second

The Presbyterian minister of Blennerhasset in Cumbria with his family and their
Fell pony in 1901.

Jet, the Dales pony bought by the BBC's *Blue Peter* programme to work with the Riding for the Disabled Association.

World War the breed was nearing extinction as so many were commandeered for the war effort and taken for artillery and pack work. (This did not generally affect the Fells, since they were under the 14.2 hands (147.3 cm) minimum height limit for remounts – although one Fell was commandeered by a remount officer, who had seen it out in the hunting field and noted its capabilities.) These demands depleted the breed to the extent that, in 1955, only four ponies, all mares, were registered and the Dales Pony Improvement Society, which had been formed in 1916, worked hard to save the breed, encouraging more people to register their foals. By the time the Dales Pony Society was formed in 1963, more ponies of better quality were being bred and registered, and the breed's resurgence as an excellent all-round ride-and-drive animal in the more affluent post-war years has seen it becoming very popular again. In the past, the Dales pony has been unfairly criticized for having lost some of its native pony character as a result of cross-breeding, but the modern Dales is a strong, active pony, full of quality and spirit and exhibiting plenty of true pony character.

THE NEW FOREST

The New Forest, which lies north of the English coast between Southampton and Bournemouth and covers around 60,000 acres (24,300 hectares), is one of the largest areas of unenclosed land in southern England and home to one of the best-known breeds of native pony. Canute's Forest Law of 1016 mentions ponies among the other wild animals of the region, and during the Middle Ages a royal stud was maintained there. In 1217 the warden of the stud was ordered by Henry III to give the annual profits accruing from the droves of ponies towards the building of Beaulieu Abbey for a period from that date until 1220. This would suggest that the ponies were sufficiently numerous and of a size and strength to be useful enough for them to constitute a regular and appreciable income to the Crown.

As so many important thoroughfares pass through the New Forest, its lack of isolation has meant that the ponies have been the subject of constant influxes of outside blood to improve them, this process apparently beginning in 1220, when eighteen Welsh pony mares were sent there. Throughout the Middle Ages, reigning European monarchs frequently gave each other horses, usually stallions, to cement alliances or seek favours, and many unwanted gifts to British monarchs were turned out on the New Forest. In Tudor times, horses from Spain and the Low Countries were imported specifically to improve the local stock, emphasizing yet again the influence of these two major Continental horse-breeding areas on the equine stock of the British Isles. During the following Stuart dynasty, the daughter of James I reputedly had a New Forest pony to ride.

In the eighteenth century, Marske, sire of the famous racehorse, Eclipse, was kept by a farmer in the New Forest for four years up until 1769 and used on New Forest mares as he was deemed too small to race. However, once Eclipse became famous, Marske was taken off for more lucrative stud work. A description of New Forest ponies written by William Gilpin in 1791 says: 'in general, the croup of the Forest horse is low, and his head ill set on, having what the jockeys call stiff jaw', although he does concede that some specimens were of much better quality.

In the nineteenth century, Queen Victoria followed the old tradition of monarchs sending stock to the New Forest, although in this case she was not abandoning an unwanted gift. Initially, she lent an Arab stallion, Zorah, to run on the forest for eight years – although his influence was believed to be minimal as the Commoners were reluctant to use him on their mares because they felt the Deputy Surveyor of the Forest had only sought to borrow him to appease the Commoners for the loss of winter grazing rights.

By 1880, however, the breed was in serious decline owing to the policy of selling good ponies and breeding from what was left, and two more Arab stallions loaned by Queen Victoria joined a number of stallions hired from elsewhere to improve the quality of ponies being bred. The Society for the Improvement of New Forest Ponies, later known as the Lyndhurst Society, was set up in 1891 to run a Spring Stallion Show and award premiums to approved stallions to run on the forest. Oddly, stallions of Russian or Polish blood were to be disqualified from receiving premiums, suggesting that outside blood from some unusual sources was being used at this time. On the other hand, the Norfolk-bred Hackney stallion, Pick Up, winner at the 1886 and 1888 Hackney Show and described as 'the beau ideal of a cob stallion', ended his days in Hampshire where he was sent to cover New Forest mares. In 1906 The Burley and District New Forest Pony and Cattle Breeding Society was formed to begin registering stock, and their first stud book was published in 1910. At that time the policy was to improve the breed with stallions from other native breeds rather than with Arabs, Thoroughbreds and polo pony stallions, and in 1893 Lord Arthur Cecil brought to the forest a number of ponies from the Scottish island of Rhum (owned at that time by his father, the Marquis of Salisbury) as well as Fells,

Farriers Finger Print, a New Forest pony bred and exhibited by Mrs. S. Young, twice winner of the NFU Ridden Mountain and Moorland championship at the National Pony Society Show.

Exmoors, Dartmoors and Welsh ponies. At the 1914 New Forest Stallion Show there were nine Welsh, five Dartmoors, four Highlands and three Exmoors among the 121 entries. In 1938 the two local societies amalgamated to become The New Forest Pony Breeding and Cattle Society and since 1935 the stud book has been closed and no outside blood has been permitted as breeders strived to achieve consistency of type within the breed.

Since 1911 a point-to-point for New Forest ponies has been held on Boxing Day, with riders weighed and ponies measured to determine handicapping for the mile and a half (2.4 km) race across the forest.

The New Forest itself is managed by the Court of Verderers, five of whom are elected and five appointed, who are funded by 'marking fees' for their services and who in turn appoint agisters (originally officials of royal forests responsible for livestock management), to look after the stock on the forest. The ponies are actually owned by Commoners, i.e. people who have common grazing rights on the forest, and the verderer's duties include the inspection of stallions to run on it. At the end of the Second World War there were about 1,200 ponies running on the forest in small herds, often divided further into smaller family groups, but this figure has now risen to around 3,000.

THE EXMOOR

While the New Forest may not be the purest-bred of the recognized native pony breeds, the Exmoor is the very opposite and is the breed which has changed least over the centuries. Exmoor ponies were mentioned in the *Domesday Book* of 1086 and continued to run out on the open expanse of the moor until, with the passing of the Enclosures Act at the beginning of the nineteenth century, the ponies were gathered and sold at a dispersal sale in 1818. Fortunately, the last Warden of the Exmoor Royal Forest, Sir Richard Acland, drove 400 of the ponies to his own land on Winsford Hill beforehand, and they formed the foundation stock for his famous Acland herd which has survived, albeit in smaller numbers, to the present day. Other ponies purchased at the dispersal sale by ancestors of many of today's breeders were instrumental in establishing other pure-bred herds, helping to save the breed from being lost through the cross-breeding which was rife during the nineteenth century. Although the cross-bred progeny struggled to survive the severe conditions of Exmoor and were often sold (therefore having little long-term effect on the pure stock), the policy of cross-breeding took many valuable mares out of the pure-bred pool. A mongrel herd of part-bred Exmoors lived for some years on the Quantock Hills to the east of Exmoor and, although the climate is milder there, the young stock still had to be taken off the hills for the winter as it is unlikely they

Exmoor mares and foals exhibiting the similarity of type that, maintained over successive generations, defines a *breed* over a *type*.

could have coped with severe weather. However, one or two cross-breds were exceptional, including The Colonel (whose sire was a part-bred Exmoor), who won the Grand National in 1869 and 1870, and the race was won in 1883 by a horse whose sire, New Oswestry, had Exmoor blood in his veins.

The pure-bred Exmoors survived the bleak years of the Great War and the Exmoor Pony Society was formed in 1921, but the Second World War saw the Exmoor, like so many other pony breeds, perilously close to extinction with only a few pure-bred mares left on the moor. Although the Exmoor is still numerically a rare breed, its unique characteristics have attracted the attention of many new enthusiasts and breeders in recent years and there are now a number of studs in other parts of Britain as well as abroad. Because the Exmoor breeds so true to type, it is one of the easiest breeds to recognize, and Exmoors are capable of carrying a significant weight in relation to their size. They make excellent all-round ride-and-drive ponies, and Evelyn March-Phillips, writing in 1896, recalls seeing a costermonger's cart drawn by an Exmoor pony overtaking a smart coachman-driven carriage and pair in Belgrave Square, noting 'on the flank of the plucky little steed the familiar anchor' (the brand that denoted a pony of the famous Acland herd).

THE DARTMOOR

The rugged terrain of Dartmoor in the south-west of England is generally considered to be poorer grazing than Exmoor, and its deep bogs, combes, granite tors and rocky slopes have, like so many other breed terrains, defined the character and resilience of the ponies that have survived there for centuries. The first mention of a Dartmoor pony in any written records appears in 1012 in the will of a Saxon bishop, Aelfwold of Crediton, and two centuries later it cost two pence a year to pasture a pony on the moor. It was not until much later, in the heyday of tin mining, that the ponies were used extensively for carrying the tin ore (and also wool) to the ports on the Devon coast, as well as undertaking some light work around the local farms, that they attained any relative value.

Up until the end of the nineteenth century, the ponies were not registered and type varied considerably. Writing in 1859, Youatt said: 'There is on Dartmoor a race of ponies much in request in that vicinity, being sure-footed and hardy, and admirably calculated to scramble over the rough roads and dreary wilds of that mountainous district. The Dartmoor pony is larger than the Exmoor and, if possible uglier'. Evidently, the ponies he was describing must have been the cross-bred mongrel animals known to have run on parts of the moor at that time, since a painting by James Loder dated 1841 of a boy on his Dartmoor pony shows a quality animal of true Dartmoor type. The breed suffered badly during the First World War, and at the same time the Duchy of Cornwall began buying up ponies for a breeding programme aimed at producing a larger stamp of riding pony by cross-breeding. However, one stallion, Dwarka, a 14.1 hands (145 cm) bay desert-bred Arab noted for having a 'pony' head, had considerable beneficial influence on the breed with many of today's best ponies tracing their pedigrees back to him. Indeed, all present-day Dartmoors are decended from The Leat, a son of Dwarka, foaled in 1918. Although not actually pure-bred, The Leat was considered to be the model Dartmoor in terms of toughness and beauty and, despite standing at stud for just three seasons and having only eight progeny registered in the stud book, he exerted considerable influence on the breed. (In the 1950s, the Dartmoor Pony Society, which had been founded twenty-five years earlier, presented a mare, Juniper, to H. M. The Queen to be ridden by Prince Charles, and Juniper was by a famous stallion called Jude, whose dam was out of The Leat's daughter, Juliet – although Jude's sire was a Welsh Mountain pony stallion called Dinarth Spark.)

Mrs. Heather Prescott's Dartmoor gelding, Micklehill Ace Amour.

Since 1898 the National Pony Society has maintained a section in its stud books for Dartmoors, and registrations increased encouragingly in the 1920s but, while the earlier practice of turning Shetland stallions out on Dartmoor with the intention of breeding pit ponies had previously threatened the breed, the Second World War hit the breed even harder as Dartmoor was used as a military training area. However, although the quality of stock on the moor declined during this period, the purity of the breed was safeguarded by more responsible breeders, who ensured its survival.

In 1898, when Dartmoors were first included in Volume V of the NPS stud book, the height limit for the breed was 14 hands (142 cm) for stallions and 13.2 hands (137 cm) for mares – although few measured that height and any that did were certainly not pure-bred. With no outside blood introduced since the beginning of the twentieth century, greater conformity with the breed standard drawn up in 1899 has been achieved overall. At present, annual registrations stand at around 200.

Dartmoors have been exported to many countries, including America, where the first imports were used to breed polo ponies and improve local stock – although there are now a number of pure-bred studs in the United States.

WELSH PONIES

Ponies have roamed the hills of Wales since time immemorial, one of the earliest records being found in the chronicles of a Welshman called Gerald who accompanied Bishop Baldwin on his travels through Wales in 1138 when the cleric was trying to muster recruits for the Crusades. According to Gerald: 'the hills of that country were full of horses'. Youatt, whose observations on the pony stock of Britain were often less than complimentary, said: 'The Welsh pony is one of the most beautiful little animals that can be imagined. He has a small head, high withers, deep yet round barrel, short joints, flat legs and good round feet. He will live on any fare and never tire.' Welsh ponies were used for all types of work, and Nimrod in his book *The Horse and the Hound*, published in 1842, quotes an example of the Welsh ponies' stamina and speed when 'a pony was ridden ten miles in forty-seven minutes, and taking thirty leaps in his course, for a wager of 1,000 guineas'. The head groom of one London dairy between the two World Wars reported turning out ninety Welsh ponies in floats every morning, adding that they were always as sound as bells.

Welsh ponies incorporate a range of types and the stud book is divided into four sections to accommodate them. Section A is the Welsh Mountain pony which, not exceeding 12 hands (122 cm), is the smallest. It was influenced by an infusion of oriental stallions early in its history, which accounts for the 'Araby' look of many of the best ponies. During the nineteenth century, one or two breeders made further introductions of Arab blood, which the breed was able to assimilate without any loss of pony character. Some Section A ponies in the recent past were bred to be finer-boned, with 'breedy' rather than pony quality, in the belief that this made them more suitable as lead-rein and first ridden ponies, but the true Section A has always had ample bone and substance. Semi-feral herds can still be found grazing on land over 1,500 feet (450 m) above sea-level.

The Welsh Section B pony can stand up to 13.2 hands (137 cm) and should be built on very similar lines to its smaller relative, the additional size having been achieved through the judicious introduction of Thoroughbred and Arab blood to produce a pony of riding type, but without any loss of native character. Although many excellent Section B ponies are bred and shown, a great many lack the substance and native character which is so imperative, and it is unlikely that some of these lighter-framed ponies could ever survive a winter on the Welsh hills.

The Section C or Welsh pony of cob type, which stands up to 13.2 hands (137 cm), and the Section D Welsh Cob, which must exceed that height, were both bred up from the Welsh Mountain pony with the addition of Spanish Andalusian and destrier blood, both of which were introduced

Welsh Section A ponies owned by Mr. and Mrs. I. Le Marquand competing in the private driving class at the Great Yorkshire Show.

Mr. John Robinsons two-year-old Welsh Section B filly, Krypton Inspiration.

Mr. and Mrs. R. E. Mills' Welsh Section C pony, Oakvale Rowan.

Mr. J. Dobson's palomino Welsh Section D Cob, St. Helen's Regency Katie, a prolific winner in harness classes.

into Wales in Norman times. The term 'cob' generally refers to a *type* of animal rather than a specific breed, the Welsh Cob being the exception. Welsh cattle drovers who made regular trips to the east coast were responsible for introducing Hackney blood into Wales, and it is likely that the characteristic trotting action came from this source. Four stallions had particular influence on the Welsh Cob: Alonzo the Brave, foaled in 1866, a bay horse standing 15.3 hands (160 cm) and a direct descendant of Old Shales, was a pure-bred Hackney; True Briton, bred in Clydogau, Wales in 1830 by John Walters, was out of an Arab mare by a Yorkshire Coach Horse; Trotting Comet, a 15.2 hands (157.5 cm) horse, foaled in 1836 and 'famous throughout Wales as a sire', was by Flyer, a well-known trotting horse; and Cymro Lloyd, a dun, was said to be by an imported Arab out of a trotting mare. All four stallions were registered in the *Hackney Stud Book*, where for many years Welsh Cobs were also registered, indicating the close links between the two breeds at that time.

Writing in 1900 about the horses of Montgomeryshire and looking back over a period of sixty years, one observer noted: 'Size has been obtained by crossing with larger sires, principally with more of the Yorkshire than of Norfolk blood', indicating possible infusions of blood from further north too. Three hundred years earlier, Daniel Defoe had written of Montgomeryshire: 'This country is noted for an excellent breed of Welsh horses, which, though not very large, are exceedingly valuable, and much esteem'd all over England', a sentiment that persisted for David Evans, the noted Welsh breeder, writing around 1905, who reported that 'cobs by registered Hackney stallions out of little Welsh mares and cob mares have lately been selling for up to 500 guineas'.

In addition to Montgomeryshire it was said that there were two major cob-breeding areas in Wales: Cardiganshire and Pembrokeshire, which produced the larger cob, and Breconshire and Radnorshire, which produced the smaller pony of cob type. In old documents, the Welsh Cob was not infrequently referred to as the Welsh Cart Horse or the Powys Cob, and was renowned as an all-round utility animal for all manner of work. In former days, Welsh Cobs were bred for trotting races as much as for work and one particular individual, Comet, foaled in 1851, once trotted 10 miles (16 km) in thirty-three minutes carrying 12 st (76 kg). Foreign governments at one time bought large numbers of young Welsh Cob stallions for breeding army horses, and many were requisitioned by the British Government during the First World War, when they coped admirably drawing gun limbers or serving as remounts or pack horses.

The Welsh Pony and Cob Society was established in 1901 by farmers, breeders and landowners who recognized the importance of documenting and recording the pedigrees of the Welsh ponies and cobs, which had traditionally been handed down by word of mouth. The Society, which is now the largest of Britain's horse and pony breed societies, published its first stud book in 1902 and the current stud books include a section for part-bred Welsh ponies with not less than 25 per cent registered Welsh blood in their veins.

The immense popularity of the Welsh pony has led to the proliferation of studs in all parts of Britain, and also in most European countries and America and Canada, and the breed has had a huge influence on many other breeds and types, including riding ponies, hacks, Hackney ponies, and many of the other mountain and moorland breeds.

THE HACKNEY PONY

The Hackney pony is the only non-native pony breed in the British Isles and it was created by one man, Christopher Wilson of Westmorland, in the 1870s. The term 'Hackney pony' had previously been in common use for some time although it was applied to a variety of pony types, some of which were undersized Hackney horses while others had no Hackney blood at all. Even the Hackney Horse Society, which was formed in 1878, seemed unsure of definitions and, at its 1886 show, second prize in the class for 'Hackney stallions not exceeding 13.3 hands high [140 cm]' was won by Lord Zetland, a Shetland pony owned by the Marquis of Bath. At one time, there was even a class for 'Hackney stallions not exceeding 10 hands [101.6 cm]' at the Hackney Show, none of which could have been Hackneys.

The Hackney pony, Sunbeam Victory, owned by Mr. G. van Nispen from Holland and driven by Anneka Huckereide to win the Supreme championship at the 2007 Hackney Show.

Christopher Wilson's aim was to produce a harness pony with quality, substance, stamina, extravagant action, tremendous presence and plenty of *pony* character. He specifically did not want to breed small horses like the so-called Hackney ponies being produced by other breeders. By using a 14 hands (142 cm) roadster stallion, Sir George, who carried both Norfolk and Yorkshire blood, on carefully selected Fell and Welsh mares, Wilson had, within a relatively short time, created the Hackney pony as we know it today. Wilson favoured a highly intensive policy of inbreeding his ponies, sire to daughter, in the belief that it would impress upon them the stamp and action of Sir George, discourage the ponies from growing any bigger, and minimize the risk of throwbacks to the full-size Hackneys from which Sir George was ultimately descended. To help reinforce the height restriction, the foals were stabled for their first winter then turned out on the Rigmaden moors to live as their native ancestors had done. The success of these ponies was immediate – there are now studs in many countries abroad – and the breed has influenced a number of others by introducing quality and improving action. In the not-too-distant past, many Hackney ponies were criticized for having degenerated into whippet-like creatures with no body or substance, bred solely for action, but fortunately this trend seems to be reversing.

THE ERISKAY PONY

In February 1972 an association was formed to try to save the Eriskay pony of Scotland which was on the brink of extinction, being described as the last survivor of the numerous native types of the Western Scottish islands known as the Hebrides (although the ponies on the island of Rhum are still extant). The Eriskay pony is said to be of ancient origin and probably based on Celtic and Norse blood, and it has a close relationship to the now-extinct ponies bred on many of the other Western Isles which were sufficiently numerous at one time for the Highland Pony Society, in its infancy, to recognize both an island and a mainland type of pony – although it did not differentiate between them in its stud books. The Eriskay Pony Society has made great progress in identifying and registering ponies of authentic Eriskay type, so many having been lost through cross-breeding, sometimes with heavy horses from the mainland, to produce larger, heavier ponies for farm and general work. Eriskay ponies are invariably grey with no white markings, and stand on average around 12.2 hands (127 cm) high. Short-coupled and strong, they exhibit all the characteristics of a breed which has evolved to survive in a hostile climate, including a dense, waterproof coat and an abundant mane and tail.

THE GYPSY PONY

Excluding the so-called Lundy pony, which was an admixture of native breeds produced on the island of Lundy in the Bristol Channel and insufficiently distinct to warrant consideration as a *breed*, and the British Spotted Pony, which is a colour pattern more than a distinct breed, there is still one type of pony which has been bred to a relatively consistent stamp in Britain for many centuries. Not having any written records or a society to promote and safeguard it, it has never been recognized as a breed – although it most probably fulfils all the criteria for one.

The coloured ponies beloved of Gypsies and travelling people have conformed to a recognized standard for at least 150 years and can be traced back to Elizabethan times when Gypsies first came to Britain from mainland Europe. Living in tents and carrying their possessions by pack pony, they established a reputation for being shrewd horsemen and dealers by buying and selling those ponies rejected by more discriminating customers. The Gypsies also used their wiles to get their mares covered by the impressive imported heavy stallions, one or two of which were coloured, by slipping their in-season mares through the fences of the royal breeding parks under cover of darkness, ensuring they recovered them

Gypsy ponies have developed into a relatively consistent type over many generations, despite the lack of a written breed standard.

again before first light. The resulting progeny evolved into the light draught stamp of animal we know today as the Gypsy pony which, despite the absence of any kind of written standard of excellence, has been bred with consistency for generations by people who have passed down the details of bloodlines as an oral tradition.

In the wake of the coaching era and with a good network of roads on which to travel, the Gypsies gave up living in tents and using pack ponies and turned instead to using horse-drawn caravans. Today, their ponies stand on average 13.2–14.2 hands (137–147.3 cm) high, as smaller animals would be unable to pull a caravan and larger animals would require more keep without there being any compensatory benefits. Well-marked coloured animals have a greater value than whole-coloured ponies, the

Gypsies' love of coloured ponies being not without reason. Distinctly coloured animals are easily recognizable and less vulnerable to theft and, in times when piebalds and skewbalds were unfashionable, they were more readily available at reasonable prices than animals of more conservative colours. Also, rather exotic and unusual colours fitted in well with the image of Gypsies who declared they were descended from the Pharoahs, their name being derived from 'Egyptian' (although they actually originated in Northern India).

The best of these animals show pony character, although some of the larger ones can be quite plain with rather coarse heads and, as with all harness breeds, some examples are straighter in the shoulder and more upright in the pasterns than would be desirable in a riding pony. The action is straight and ground-covering but with some knee and hock action. The formation in recent years of societies for coloured horses and ponies and the opening of an export market for these ponies is likely to see the Gypsy pony's popularity increase further, and there are now excellent competitive opportunities for coloured ponies across a range of equestrian disciplines.

While the breeds mentioned in this chapter are extant, they are far outnumbered by those breeds which have been lost, mainly over the last two centuries, and which can never be recreated again. Some of these will be discussed in the next chapter.

Chapter 7

BREEDS UNDER THREAT

When the last individual of a race of living things breathes no more, another heaven and earth must pass before such a one can be again.
WILLIAM BEEBE, 1906

According to the *World Dictionary of Livestock Breeds*, in 1988 there were nearly 500 horse and pony breeds in the world, a further ninety breeds had become extinct in very recent times, twenty more breeds were on the verge of becoming extinct, and another seventy were so low in numbers that they were likely to disappear in the foreseeable future. In the British Isles, the conservative and parochial tradition of 'local breeds for local needs' produced more distinct races of agricultural livestock, including equines, than any other similarly sized country in the world, and the isolation of breeding areas for feral native ponies just added to the overall diversity by supporting regional variation. Writing early in the nineteenth century, an equestrian commentator noted: 'As to the English pony, almost every district has its breed', leading another writer of the time to speculate that there could have been as many as fifty regional horse and pony types in the British Isles, of which only around 20 per cent survive today. This chapter will address various factors that have been brought to bear on British native stock. These are often complex and frequently interwoven – and it is sometimes the case that apparently negative factors had certain positive influences, while well-intentioned initiatives sometimes had detrimental effects.

HISTORICAL LACK OF RECOGNITION

The reason for the loss of breeds can be partly attributed to a general failure in the past to recognize and value the worth of individual breeds. As William Scarth Dixon noted in 1915:

'It is so self-evident that in our native mountain and moorland pony breeds we have a most valuable national asset that it almost seems necessary to apologize for referring to such a fact. Yet not so many years ago the native breeds were, generally speaking, but little thought of.'

Evidence of that is legion. One earlier observer condemned Exmoor and Dartmoor ponies as: 'arrant jades, ill-made, large-headed, short-necked, and ragged hipped, one more ugly than another', while a contributor to the *Sporting Magazine* in 1831 described Exmoors as having: 'a shaggy coat, immense pot belly, short ewe neck, big head, ragged mane and tail, 12 to 14 hands, and the Dartmoor larger and even uglier than the Exmoors'. The latter comment cannot have referred to pure-bred ponies because of the reference to their size, yet the criticism was applied indiscriminately. One of the most influential equestrian writers of his day, Youatt, writing in 1859 said: 'The Exmoor ponies, although ugly enough, are hardy and useful'. His words seem to reflect the views of other influential writers of the time including J. H. Walsh who, in 1862, wrote: 'The Welsh pony is extremely disposed to be obstinate', and went on to suggest that the New Forest pony was 'more useful than ornamental, and not too highly gifted with the former quality either', adding that the Highland pony had 'cat hams like the old Welsh breed'. Significantly, Walsh defined British horses and ponies by their roles rather than by their breed. Three years later W. J. Miles listed only Shetlands, Galloways, Dartmoors, Welsh, New Forest and Highland ponies (which he notes as being 'not pleasant to ride, except in the canter'), among the pony breeds – although all the existing horse breeds are mentioned. It is therefore no wonder that, with so little value attributed to them, formerly renowned breeds like the Devon Pack Horse, Galloway pony, Yorkshire Coach Horse, Fen pony, Vardy horse, Goonhilly and many more were allowed to become extinct within a relatively short span of time.

The general lack of recognition of the *worth* of many breeds was compounded by the fact that, up until the nineteenth century, relatively few

Many Victorian children learnt to ride on native ponies, in this case a Dartmoor, but generally the breeds were little thought of, which is why so many were allowed to slip into extinction.

breeds were recognized as such. Instead there were regional 'types' usually identified by their geographical location such as Fen pony, Galloway and Yorkshire Trotter but, in the same way that not all cattle from Hereford belong to the Hereford breed, the descriptions of individual ponies in records from the past are often misleading. For example, so famous did the now-extinct Galloway pony of south-west Scotland become that the term 'Galloway' came to signify a small, active riding horse or pony and, in the mid-nineteenth century a race for ponies under 14 hands (142 cm) was held in Devon and advertised as a 'Galloway Race', although it is exceedingly unlikely that any of the runners were representatives of the Scottish breed. With no breed societies before the late nineteenth century to draw up breed standards, inspect and pass animals as suitable for registration, maintain stud books and encourage the breeding and marketing of quality stock, animals were at risk of cross-breeding or of being absorbed into other breeds under the principle of the old saying: 'A good horse has no race.' Bearing in mind that for nearly a thousand years, size and strength had been the main goals in all organized horse-breeding programmes, the concept of a *pure breed* was alien to most horsemen of the time and, technically, very few breeds can claim to be of absolutely pure descent with no alien blood introduced over the centuries at all.

Even when breed societies came into being, controversy frequently arose between breeders as to what defined an accepted standard for each breed, making it difficult to achieve agreement on correct type, with the inherent risk that influential committee members could do more harm than good. At a Fell Pony Stallion Show held at Middleton in Teesdale in 1920, the two judges could not agree over a champion. One judge, Mr. Tom Bainbridge from Brough, favoured Sporting Times, a skewbald pony, while the other judge, Mr. R. B. Charlton from Hexham, went for Hilton Fashion, a grey, as he contended that a piebald or skewbald could not be of pure Fell pony blood. At length, a third man was brought into the ring as referee judge to adjudicate between the two ponies. The referee judge had been drinking in the local pub and was very much the worse for it, but he staggered into the ring, swaying visibly. Without even looking at the ponies, he pointed with his stick and in a loud, drunken voice shouted: 'Gee it to Baldie!', and the decision was made. Such incidents were not uncommon, and the early stud books for all the breeds contain anomalies in terms of ponies registered as pure-bred when they evidently were not (including several Arabs registered as Connemaras), and the breed societies and their inspection officers had to tread a fine line in discouraging registration of ponies which did not conform to the breed standard while not putting breeders off the whole concept of registering ponies at a time when many saw it as an expense with few or no benefits.

CHANGING NEEDS AND ABSORPTION INTO OTHER BREEDS

Cross-breeding to meet new market demands or the insatiable export trade were not the biggest culprits in the demise of so many old breeds. Another reason was changing needs. In some cases, where the main uses of a breed became outmoded, this led directly to its demise. Examples include the Cornish pony, a utility breed held in high regard in the West Country and sometimes known as the Goonhilly or Bodmin Moor pony from two of its main breeding areas, described by Richard Carew in 1602 as: 'hardly bred, coarsely fed, low stature, quick in travel, and able enough for continuance, which sort prove most serviceable for a rough and hilly country'. Another now-extinct breed, the Manx pony, was similarly bred to suit local needs on the Isle of Man, and there were other regional types which developed and eventually died out without ever having left their home ground.

In other cases, certain qualities of a breed led to its absorption into a new breed and, less directly, to the demise of the original form. For example, the Devon Pack Horse, a once-famous West Country breed which was actually a pony rather than a horse, bred up from Exmoor stock, slipped into obscurity when railways ousted the pack trains, and the Devon Cob, similar to the Devon Pack Horse but bred up from Dartmoor pony stock, followed it into extinction. But when the Chapman horse of Yorkshire was no longer needed as a pack and general utility farm horse, its descendant, the Cleveland Bay, found a niche as a harness horse and was especially popular with professional coachmen. Writing about the Chapman or Yorkshire Pack Horse, Vero Shaw, the agricultural writer, said: 'It was most unquestionably a valuable breed and hence regret must be expressed that it was ever permitted to become extinct.' However, as explained in Chapter 5, the Cleveland Bay became so popular for carriage work or as a coach horse that it produced an off-shoot breed, the Yorkshire Coach Horse, in the nineteenth century. Despite having a breed society since 1886, the Yorkshire Coach Horse was essentially a sustained cross of Cleveland Bay and Thoroughbred blood, sometimes with a splash of Hackney – as the breeding of Yorkshire Coach Horses was not an exact science. The resulting horse was bigger, lighter and flashier than the more utilitarian Cleveland Bay and ideal for the elegant carriages of fashionable cities, as well as being faster on the road and better suited for the new roads with toll gates introduced from the time of George II onwards.

Remarkable feats of endurance were achieved by Yorkshire Coach Horses, one example named Pierson's Plato trotting 18 miles (29 km) in one hour carrying 18 st (114 kg). However, with the coming of motor vehicles the breed soon lost its market and by the 1930s the Yorkshire Coach Horse and the society which had supported it had gone forever. As Jack Fairfax-Blakeborough said: 'The purpose of the Yorkshire Coach Horse has now gone, but the history of its creation is an outstanding example of Man's power to produce and mould to his desire a fixed equine type.' Ironically, Cleveland Bay/Thoroughbred crosses, which are to all intents and purposes Yorkshire Coach Horses, have excelled in other equestrian disciplines more recently, although they are now classed as a cross rather than a separate breed.

Another tough and useful breed which disappeared after attempts to modify it for agricultural use failed was the Galloway. This breed originated in the south-west of Scotland and shared similar origins to the Fell pony, as Christopher Wilson, originator of the Hackney pony, noted when he wrote: 'The old Galloway was the same as the Fell pony, only it showed a little more breeding.' In his *Tour Through Scotland,* written in 1706, Daniel Defoe said of the horses of the Galloway region of south-west Scotland: 'they have the best breed of strong, low horses in Britain, if not Europe, which we call pads, and from whence we call *all* truss-strong small riding horses Galloways'. Dr. Anderson, writing at around the same time, said: 'There was once a breed of small elegant horses in Scotland, similar to those of Iceland and Sweden, and which were known by the name of Galloway.' His use of the past tense would indicate they were in decline even then, and Youatt, writing in 1851, confirms this when he notes that they are: 'now sadly degenerated through the attempts of the farmer to obtain a larger kind, better adapted for the purpose of agriculture'. Standing up to 14 hands (142 cm) in height, they were renowned for their extraordinary stamina. Scottish cattle drovers used them extensively for journeys of up to several hundred miles on very meagre rations, and a Galloway pony belonging to Dr. Anderson carried him on his travels for twenty-five years, during which time he twice rode the pony on a 150-mile (241 km) journey without stopping except for meal breaks, which never lasted for more than an hour. 'It came in at the last stage', wrote the doctor, 'with as much ease and alacrity as it travelled the first.' Another exceptional feat had been performed at Carlisle in 1701, when a Galloway pony belonging to a man called Sinclair from Kirkby Lonsdale travelled 1,000 miles (1,609 km) in the same number of hours. Fifty-three years later, a pony of the same breed belonging to a sportsman called Corker did 100 miles (160 km) a day for three consecutive days over the Newmarket course. Sir Walter Gilbey quoted Youatt in his book, *Thoroughbred and other Ponies*, published in 1903, saying of Galloways:

> The purposes for which they were used indicated the desirability of increasing their height and strength, and with this end in view cross-breeding was commenced somewhere about the year eighteen hundred and continued for fifty

years. The Galloway after this period almost disappeared from all parts of the mainland, and survives only in such remote situations as the Island of Mull.

One breed which was absorbed into the make-up of another breed was the Norfolk Farm Horse (also known as the Black Fen Horse or Lincolnshire Black), a strong but coarse agricultural breed, absorbed into the much-improved and better quality Shire, which soon outshone its ancestors. Another example was the Old English Black, an intermediate breed which linked the Norfolk Farm Horse to the modern Shire and upon which Henry VIII is purported to have mounted his cavalry. This breed was said to have 'increased in size and substance from the nature of the grasses of the district, which seem peculiarly adapted to develop the growth of this animal', the eastern counties being, at one time, the principle breeding area for heavy farm horses. J. H. Walsh, a former editor of *The Field*, writing in 1862 under the pseudonym 'Stonehenge', said of the Old English Black Cart Horse:

> From time immemorial this country has possessed a heavy and comparatively misshapen animal, the more active of which were formerly used as chargers or pack-horses, while the others were devoted to the plough and, as time wore on, to the lumbering vehicles of the period of Queen Elizabeth and her immediate successors. In colour almost invariably black, with a great fiddle-case in the place of a head, and feet concealed in long masses of hair, depending from misshapen legs, he united flat sides, upright shoulders, mean and narrow hips, and very drooping quarters. Still, plain as he was, he did his work willingly, and would pull at a dead weight till he dropped.

The breed survived until the late eighteenth century because there was nothing better but there can be no doubt that the early Shire, developed by Bakewell, was far superior in speed, strength and looks to the Old English Black and its antecedents and no one at the time or since has apparently mourned the loss of the old breed.

Another type, known as the Improved Lincolnshire Dray Horse, was developed from Flemish stock crossed with the Old English Black, but the breed had drawbacks as 'Stonehenge' noted:

> 'Unfortunately, both sire and dam are slow, and the produce, from its increased bulk, is rendered still slower, being wholly unfit for agricultural operations in competition with the Suffolk or Clydesdale horses, and only well adapted to move heavy brewers' drays, which cannot from their weight be expected to travel very rapidly.'

Similarly, the early Suffolk Cart Horses, which were ousted by the more active and clean-legged Suffolk Punch as we know it today, were described by Arthur Young as being capable of pulling a 5-ton (5,080 kg) load for many miles on sandy roads but 'an uglier horse cannot be viewed – it can trot no better than a cow'. Others, more diplomatically, conceded: 'Their merit probably consists more in constitutional hardiness than fine shape, being in general a very plain horse.'

The success of the Shire, Clydesdale, Suffolk and the imported French Percheron breeds saw the demise of another type bred in the north-east and once so popular as to be a contender for breed status itself. The Vardy horse was a general-purpose farm horse produced from a blend of the Bakewell Black or early Shire and the Cleveland Bay and noted for its active movement, but it died out towards the end of the nineteenth century. (The name Vardy horse was also sometimes used erroneously to describe the light 'vanner' types used by Gypsies and travelling people to pull their *vardies* or living waggons.)

While it could be argued that a loss of a breed is always a loss, it is sometimes the case that certain attributes of a breed live on in the influences they bring to bear on a new breed that, in part at least, derives from them. This could be said of the Norfolk Roadster and the Yorkshire Trotter. As mention in Chapter 5, these were two not dissimilar types of all-round utility horse which developed separately but simultaneously in two of the country's principle horse-breeding areas. Strong and active with legendary stamina and the ability to trot great distances at speed, both were essentially riding horses with the low, ground-covering stride, peculiar to that class of horse, and they contributed significantly to the Hackney horse into which they were eventually absorbed. The Norfolk Roadster and his Yorkshire-bred contemporary were linked by their common ancestry on the distaff side of Flemish and Friesian blood, which gave them many similarities in size and type, and by Thoroughbred blood through the male lines. Alexander Morton, in an address to the Glasgow Agricultural Discussion Society in 1891, in which he compared the Norfolk Roadster and the Yorkshire Trotter, said the former was 'a much heavier horse, longer in the barrel, rounder in the shoulders which, however, are as a rule better laid back. He is also plainer about the head but has generally more action, particularly behind'. Morton attributed the regional differences to more 'of the old British blood in the Norfolk Hackney'.

Another British breed that had considerable influence on the Hackney horse was the once-famous Shales, although it was in reality a strain of Norfolk Roadster descended from one outstanding stallion and found in all Hackney pedigrees today. In his book, *The History and Delineation of the Horse*, published in 1809, John Lawrence wrote: 'The best trotters which have appeared and which are to be found in Lincolnshire, Norfolk and their vicinity, have proceeded from Old Shields'. Written phonetically and frequently misspelt, the horse's name was more often written as Shales or Schales, and in his later years he was sometimes referred to as Old Shales or the Original Shales to differentiate him from his descendants of the same name. It is probable that Shales was the name of the owner, as it was customary to name horses after whoever owned them at the time, which can be confusing as a horse's name could change with his ownership. Foaled around 1755, Shales was by the Thoroughbred, Blaze, a son of the Duke of Devonshire's racehorse, Flying Childers (by the Darley Arabian) who, despite his lack of stature, distinguished himself on the racecourse before going on to make a name for himself at stud. Shales' dam was stated as being 'a strong common-bred mare', probably a farm or cart horse.

The most famous member of the strain was a grandson of Old Shales called Marshland Shales, a 15 hands (152.5 cm) chestnut with an immense crest who was foaled in 1802 and described in an issue of the *Sporting Magazine* as being 'acknowledged both the speediest and stoutest trotter of the time'. Unbeaten in the many trotting matches in which he competed, Marshland Shales' most famous match against Richard West's horse, Driver, was reported in great detail in the 6th August 1810 issue of the *Norwich Mercury*, which recorded that the great horse trotted 17 miles (27 km) in fifty-eight minutes carrying 12 st (76 kg). The Shales strain of roadster achieved great renown, and in the first volume of the Hackney Horse Society stud book published in 1889 there were over eighty stallions whose names included 'Shales'. One of the foundation stones of the Hackney horse breed was a stallion called The Norfolk Cob who, according to an article in the *Sunday Times* in 1839, was: 'Out of a Shields mare, and reputed to be the fastest trotter that ever stepped'. Shales blood also found its way into a number of native breeds, primarily the Fell, Dales and Welsh Cob, before being absorbed into the Hackney and virtually disappearing from other breeds – although occasionally horses claimed to be direct pure descendants of the old Shales breed still turn up.

LOSS OF HABITAT

Loss of habitat is a problem which has affected many of the pony breeds over a protracted period. The Enclosures Act, which resulted in a huge decrease in common grazing land, coupled with the increased use of what common grazing was left for hill cattle and sheep (which were economically far more profitable than ponies), initiated a gradual reduction in semi-feral free-roaming herds of ponies which began in the early nineteenth century and has continued to this day. The controversial issue of allowing stallions and colts of inferior quality to run on common grazing (a problem which Henry VIII's statutes had tried to address in the sixteenth century), has also

The Norfolk Cob, one of the foundation stones of the Hackney breed and, according to the *Sunday Times* in 1839, 'the fastest trotter that ever stepped'.

continued ever since, despite attempts by various bodies to control it. Many of the pony-breeding areas in Wales, for example, organized their own Pony Improvement Societies, and the passing of the 1908 Commons Act gave them the support they needed to rid the commons of undesirable stallions. Pony breeders in the area around Church Stretton in Shropshire realized the need to improve the ponies running on the Long Mynd hills, and the Improvement Society they formed took responsibility for rounding up the semi-feral breeding stock, removing inferior animals and turning out better quality stallions. This resulted in such a vast improvement that the Long Mynd strain earned considerable renown before eventually being absorbed into the Welsh pony breed.

The draining of the fenlands of Lincolnshire for agricultural use robbed another breed, the Fen pony, of its native habitat. Believed to have developed from Friesian horses of the roadster rather than draught type, brought over by Dutch drainage experts from the early seventeenth century and crossed with small local pony mares, the Fen pony was fast disappearing by the mid-nineteenth century when it was reported by Youatt that: 'A great many ponies, of little value, used to be reared in Lincolnshire, in the neighbourhood of Boston; but the breed has been neglected for some years, and the enclosure of the fens will render it extinct.' Described as seldom reaching 13 hands (132 cm), 'the head was large and the forehand low, the back straight, the leg flat and good, but the foot, even for a Lincolnshire pony, unnaturally large. They were applied to very inferior purposes even on the fens, and were unequal to hard and flinty and hilly roads'. In a pamphlet on Highland ponies written by Thomas Dykes in 1905 he concludes: 'the superiority of Scottish hill-bred horses for active work as against the ancient Fen types, seems to have been very early established in relation to the trade in horses between Scotland and the south of England which was largely dependent on the Scottish cattle drovers'. Like many regional breeds, Fen ponies were best suited to their own locality and, when no longer needed, could not adapt to other terrain.

THE EXPORT MARKET

Horse breeds have long been at risk from having their breeding numbers depleted by foreign buyers who, since Tudor times, had realized the value of British horses and initiated an export trade that reached its peak in the nineteenth century. A House of Commons Select Committee was even formed to address the situation in 1873, and Joshua East, a London horse dealer and jobmaster who never had less than around a thousand horses in his extensive stables, told the committee that French agents: 'buy the best and they get mares. You cannot get them to buy a bad mare'. The export in breeding stock extended to many other European countries, with the Italian Government buying seventy Hackney stallions in 1890, and a contract being negotiated, but never signed, for the purchase of another 600 over a period of six years. In addition to Europe, there was much interest from further afield: in 1888, twenty-eight Hackney stallions were exported to South Africa, and other interested customers included Finland, Russian, Japan, America, Australia and New Zealand.

Following a meeting between representatives of the Hackney, Cleveland Bay and Yorkshire Coach Horse Societies in 1887 to discuss the impact of a proposed Government grant on the fortunes of their respective breeds, the Press reported: 'Their value had long since been ascertained by foreigners, who had been quietly and systematically buying up the best of them, then selling their progeny to the English Government for the use of the army.' It was even speculated in some quarters that some of Britain's oldest horse breeds would only survive on foreign soil, having had breeding numbers reduced considerably on home ground.

MILITARY DEPLOYMENT

Over the centuries, British monarchs and governments had maintained an interest in the production of horses and ponies suitable for use in warfare, and various breeding programmes had been introduced down the years with that aim in mind. Protracted campaigns, such as in the era of the Napoleonic Wars, made immense demands of the equine population, often with highly detrimental effects, as in the case of the Irish Hobby.

The Irish Hobby had been in existence as a recognizable type for several centuries when Richard Berenger wrote in 1771 that they were: 'valued for their easy paces, and other pleasing and agreeable qualities, of middling size, strong, nimble, well-moulded and hardy.' Another writer of the time, Charles Smith, had written in his *Natural and Civic History of Kerry*: 'The little hobbies of the country are the most correct horses to travel through it, and a man must abandon himself entirely to their guidance, which will answer much better than if one should strive to manage and direct their footsteps.' Although military use was not the *only* reason for their decline, it played a significant part, as pointed out by Professor E. Estyn Evans in his book, *Irish Folkways*: 'Large numbers of these little ponies were being drawn on to support the British Cavalry in the peninsular wars, used as pack ponies, and often times as meat when supplies ran out', and at the Battle of Waterloo ranks of Irish Hobbies reportedly fell under enemy fire. Professor David Low, writing in 1842, noted:

> They have lost much of the reputation which they once possessed... No care is bestowed in selection...so that it is now difficult to obtain a tolerable pony in places where a few years ago they were numerous. It will scarcely be credited that numbers of them have been recently bought by dealers to be fattened and sold as Irish beef.

This quotation points to another factor that had a profound influence on the breed. During the Irish Potato Famine of 1846, when a large proportion of the population died of starvation, many people had no choice but to eat their horses, depleting breed numbers further. It is, therefore, quite amazing that a strain of the Irish Hobby known as the Kerry Bog pony should have been recently identified and saved from extinction by a small group of breeders, whose claims of their ponies' ancestry were confirmed by DNA testing carried out by Weatherbys Ireland Ltd., resulting in the Kerry Bog pony being recognized by the Irish Horse Board, Department of Agriculture and other equine societies. In 2000, the Irish Horse Board even nominated the pony as Ireland's heritage pony for the Millennium year. Kerry Bog ponies are small, about 11.2 hands (117 cm) for stallions and 10.2–10.3 hands (approx.108 cm) for mares, and mainly chestnut, bay, brown or grey, part-colours being debarred, and a dished head reminiscent of an Arab is one of the characteristics of the breed. This strain aside, however, the Irish Hobby is no longer extant, nor is another representative of the general type, the Cushendall, which closely matched contemporary descriptions of the Galloway pony.

Following Napoleon's eventual defeat at Waterloo in 1815, the British

Government had taken stock of all horses that could potentially be requisitioned and impressed for military service in the event of another national crisis, but it was to be some years before any actual Government initiatives were introduced to further this cause. However, this did not mean that apparently unlikely 'recruits' did not sometimes get pressed into service. On July 22nd 1882, the *Daily Telegraph* reported: 'Twenty-six horses and a number of Shetland ponies from Woolwich arrived yesterday afternoon at the Wellington Barracks. They are intended for the use of the 1st Battalion of the Scots Guards stationed there.' The announcement produced considerable mirth in the Press, including a cartoon of a Scots Guard mounted on a Shetland pony – although their intended use was for specialist pack work. Five years after this quirky report, in December 1887, the *Daily Telegraph* reported: 'It was announced in the House of Commons before the close of Session that the Government proposed to make a grant of £5,000 for the purpose of encouraging the breeding of horses in England, primarily with a

Shetland ponies still maintain a military association! The Parachute Regiment's
Shetland pony mascots, Pegasus and Falklands.

view to securing a sufficient home supply for army and military use' and, as W. J. Gordon noted in 1893, there were at that time 'thousands of horses under subsidy with a view to immediate use'. By the beginning of the twentieth century the British Government had learnt that the standard stamp of troop horse used in the Boer War, when the army was losing 336 horses a day (326,000 during the entire war), had fared indifferently in combat conditions and was not up to long marches, which prompted the Parliamentary Commissions tasked to consider the problems to support a move to find remounts with a good splash of native pony blood. To this end, premiums were offered in pony-breeding areas for both mares and stallions of a type likely to produce animals suitable for mounted infantry. While this may have given the market a much needed fillip, it also encouraged cross-breeding and greatly reduced some sections of the breeding stock.

One cross-breeding proposal that fortunately did not proceed came from Professor Cossar Ewart of Edinburgh, whose studies into British native ponies were as detailed and meticulous as some of his suggestions were fatuous. He believed: 'If Connemara mares are crossed with hard, useful, unspoilt Thoroughbreds, then doubtless the progeny will be suitable for light cavalry.' His memorandum to the Government concluded with a proposal to turn all of Connemara into a giant stud farm producing a large crop of half-bred foals which, by running out on the hills, would inherit the hardiness of their dams. Fortunately, the Government did not take up his proposal which would have both seriously damaged the Connemara breed and proved futile, as half-breds would never have survived to breaking age on the exposed hills and bogs of western Ireland.

However, the encouragement of cross-breeding and its potential consequences where not the only ways in which military objectives impacted on the native breeds. In some quarters, interest had also been shown in pure-bred natives for military work and, bearing in mind that the minimum height for mounted infantry remounts in 1900 was only 13 hands (132 cm), this brought many native breeds into military compass. The New Forest Scouts, raised in 1899 as a mounted company of the 4th Battalion of the

Hampshire Volunteers, were all mounted on ponies, most of which had been bred on the forest. They were owned by the troopers, and training consisted of 30 miles (48 km) a day carrying a rider and his equipment, including a heavy army saddle. Lord Lucas wrote of the New Forest ponies used by the Scouts: 'We have a breed unsurpassed in hardiness and endurance' adding that, at the end of a 50-mile day in camp the previous year, the New Forest ponies, some only three-year-olds, were neither sick nor sorry.

One might think that involvement in the theatre of war would inevitably be bad news for any breed, but circumstances are rarely that straightforward and, certainly, some supporters of the Highland pony saw things in a different light. Writing in the early years of the twentieth century, James McDonald, Secretary of the Highland and Agricultural Society of Scotland, observed:

> For a time it looked as if the Highland Pony would also be allowed to pass out of existence. No-one seemed disposed to lift even a little finger to save it but the outbreak of the South African War and the demand for mounted infantry caused a fresh view to be taken of the utility of these hardy medium-sized animals. Since then, Highland pony breeding has become quite popular.

His words were echoed by Thomas Dykes, writing in 1905, who said: 'Until the formation of Lovat's Scouts, a mounted regiment which did admirable service in the recent campaign in South Africa, it seems highly probable that the Highland pony would be allowed to pass into oblivion.' Lord Lovat had suggested the Scouts as better reconnaissance was needed and he thought men of the Highlands, skilled in deer stalking, would be ideal. Highland ponies were again in demand during the First World War when Lord Middleton, who owned the Applecross Stud of Highland ponies, wrote:

> It may be of interest to the National Pony Society to know that six of my ponies, which went from here with the Ross-shire Mountain Battery to the war were all last winter at Bedford, then moved to Alexandria and from there to the

Dardanelles, where they have been for the last four months at the front, carrying ammunition, etc. They are all well and fat with the exception of one, Professor, that was blown to pieces by a shell. I also hear from other quarters what excellent work all these Highland Ponies from Ross-shire and Argyllshire have done.

Inevitably, Professor was not the only individual to pay the price for the promotion of his breed. At the outbreak of the First World War, The Duke of Sutherland owned a number of well-bred Highland ponies which were used in the deer forests prior to being requisitioned for war purposes, with the proviso that they would be returned afterwards if required. None ever returned to their native Scotland and most probably ended their days in Gallipoli or in the mud of Flanders.

Whole breeds that paid a high price for the ravages of war included the Welsh Cobs and Dales. These were requisitioned in high numbers for the Great War, where they excelled in the lead of four-in-hand artillery teams, and Lionel Edwards, the artist and remount officer, reported seeing hundreds of Welsh Cob mares being unloaded at Salonica, never to return to their home country. In all, this war claimed the lives of at least 375,000 horses in total and, when peace was declared, there were less than a dozen Welsh Cob stallions and twenty-five mares left in the stud book.

It was not just the native pony breeds that became involved in the Great War. So many Hackney horses were requisitioned for the war effort that the Hackney Horse Society took the unprecedented step of including two new classes in the schedule for its annual show at Newmarket for: 'Stallions suitable for breeding artillery and army horses. To be judged on conformation, true and straight action.' The winner in 1918 was Findon Grey Shales, a ten-year-old owned by H.R.H. The Prince of Wales. (The classes were discontinued after the 1927 show.)

In 1922 the War Office took over from the Department of Agriculture in the paying of premiums to suitable stallions, mostly Fells, Dales and Welsh Cobs, a practice which lasted into the 1930s, to encourage the breeding of a useful stamp of all-round troop or pack animal. Interestingly, in respect of using Fells for this purpose, Christopher Wilson, the nineteenth-century originator of the Hackney pony, had observed many years earlier that a Hackney 'would be a more suitable cross for the Fell pony to breed troopers from than the Arab. The resultant ponies would be much hardier'. In fact, during the Boer War, one squadron of the Imperial Yeomanry recruited in East Anglia had been mounted on Hackneys bred in that area and, according to a report in the *Livestock Journal*, they withstood the hardships of the campaign better than most of the other imported English horses.

Even with advancing mechanization, equine stock was again involved in the Second World War; for example Welsh Cobs were used as pack carriers, training with the Second Remount Squadron on Derby Racecourse before being issued to units of the Pack Brigade for further training in Scotland, after which they were shipped abroad, many going to Italy. Many of the men working with them were Shropshire Yeomanry from the Welsh Borders, who had worked with Welsh Cobs previously at home. Peripheral military activity, for example the military use of Dartmoor, also had an impact on native populations. At the end of the Second World War a spokesman for the National Pony Society wrote: 'The war years have depleted our stocks of native pony to such an alarming degree that that it will take all the hard work we can possibly put into it to save from extinction certain of the mountain and moorland pony breeds.'

BREEDING POLICIES AND THE EMERGENCE OF BREED SOCIETIES

It would be easy to think that attempts to 'improve' breeds would be likely to have beneficial effects but, while some have undoubtedly done this, others, especially those ill-conceived or pursued for questionable motives, have had detrimental or even dire effects.

We have already touched upon the involvement of the British

Government in some breeding initiatives during wartime, but it is unfortunate that certain peacetime interventions, although well-intentioned, were clearly unsuccessful. A prime example is The Congested Districts Board of Scotland, founded by Act of Parliament in 1898 and consisting of a secretary and a small board of advisers, which was formed to help the poorer districts in the Highlands to improve the quality of their livestock by supplying bulls, rams and stallions for the crofters. Professor Cossar Ewart, mentioned earlier in connection with his proposals regarding cross-breeding Connemaras for military use, was entrusted with selecting, breeding or purchasing suitable stallions to be used by the crofters to improve their ponies, taking into account hardiness, utility, cost of upkeep, suitability for hill work or service with the mounted infantry as well as profitability when marketed, but he was instructed to avoid Clydesdale horses or their crosses. Instead he bought ponies from Scandinavia, Connemara, Iceland and the Western Isles of Barra, Skye and Uist on which he used Arab, Thoroughbred and Highland stallions. He sent some of the Arab stallions to Skye, but the crofters made very limited use of them as they considered them unsuitable for croft work and they were soon discarded in favour of selected Highland stallions, described as typical of the breed but much undersized – which suited the smaller Skye ponies. John Macdonald, the tenant on the farm adjoining that where Professor Ewart's motley stud was sited, was able to watch 'this interesting but hopeless experiment', and was capable of foretelling its ultimate fate. In due course a member of the Board took responsibility for its livestock breeding operations and disposed of all but a few strong native pony stallions, the lesson having been learnt.

Another failed initiative occurred in Ireland around the start of the twentieth century, when many west coast Connemara breeders also saw a lucrative market in the breeding of 'agricultural' horses to sell to the more affluent farming areas in the south and east and used Clydesdale colts, provided free by the British Government, on their pony mares with disastrous results. The larger foals produced had no substance and as

Thomas Meleady, the Dublin horse dealer, reported: 'The mixture of ponies with Scotch horses that got into Galway and County Mayo ruined that country, and they are neither horses nor ponies…soft, hairy-legged bits of ponies, and no use.' In an attempt to rectify the situation, the Government provided Thoroughbred, Hackney and hunter stallions, which produced better sorts than the Clydesdale crosses, but the harsh environment defeated this initiative too for, as Bernard O'Sullivan wrote: 'We have yet to meet a specimen of the Thoroughbred, Half-bred, Hackney or Clydesdale capable of living through a winter…relying on some convenient rock or hillock for shelter from the blast.' The long-term effect was a severe reduction in the breeding pool of Connemara mares, with the old breed becoming extinct in some areas.

One example of detrimental cross-breeding that was purely commercially motivated arose from the middle of the nineteenth century onward when, in response to the insatiable demand for pit ponies, Shetland stallions were used indiscriminately on many of the smaller breeds with the sole intention of breeding animals suitable for mine work. Fortunately, the bulk of the cross-bred animals were sold off to meet the expanding market the mines created and the long-term damage to the breeds was limited. Ironically, the last pit ponies in Britain, which were retired from Ellington Colliery in Northumberland in 1994, were all pure-bred natives – two Welsh Mountains, a Dartmoor and a Fell – but the 70,000 ponies working down the mines prior to 1914 were primarily Shetland or Shetland crosses.

Looking overall at the cross-breeding initiated by Man, it would appear that the Exmoors and Shetlands escaped the work of the 'improvers' most of all (the latter not being greatly imperilled by the mine owners' requirements, for reasons just explained), followed in apparent order by the Fells, Dales, Welsh ponies, Highlands, Welsh Cobs, Connemaras, Dartmoors and New Forests in descending order – although that does not suggest a necessarily true level of cross-breeding, as many cross-breds did not survive the environment or were sold off, so the natural breeding stock was not affected long-term. Writing in 1944, Lady Wentworth rashly stated:

'Exmoor ponies are cross-bred much in the same way as other moorland ponies', referring specifically to when the Royal Forest of Exmoor was sold in 1818 to John Knight, a northern industrialist, who set about 'improving' the local ponies. He used Dongolese Arabs, a strain of Barb described by The Druid in 1862 as: 'an Arab of sixteen hands and peculiar to the region around Nubia', as well as Thoroughbreds and what were described as 'thirty half-breds of the coaching Cleveland sort'. The harsh environment of the moor, which Daniel Defoe had described in 1722 as 'a filthy barren ground', defeated his aims as the 'improved Exmoors', illustrated in *The Farmers Magazine* in 1867 and nothing like true Exmoors, could simply not survive there. Similar experiments with other native breeds often ended in failure too for, to reiterate Sir Berkeley Piggott's statement, the 'grinding-down' effect of the environment ensured that only the type that is best able to maintain and reproduce itself under the local conditions prevailed. However, throughout the centuries and right up until recent times, valuing the purity of a breed has often seemed secondary to producing what breeders felt may be a more marketable product. When Sir Walter Gilbey wrote: 'Organized efforts have been made to improve the ponies, and in Devonshire and Somerset the original strains have been intermingled and alien blood introduced and these sires have produced new and improved breeds', he could have had little idea how quickly the latter would prove unsuitable and die out. The Dartmoor ponies could be an exception, for one of the most influential stallions on the breed, a pony called The Leat and bred by the Tor Royal stud, was actually only one-quarter Dartmoor from a grand-dam whose breeding was unknown, the rest being one-quarter Roadster and one-half Arab.

Given that so many of Man's cross-breeding interventions proved detrimental, it is perhaps ironic that an intervention for an apparently trivial reason should spark a chain of events that was largely influential in the emergence of breed societies which, while not *invariably* a force for good, have had, overall, a positive influence on the protection and promotion of British Breeds. The salvation for many pony breeds heading towards extinction in the nineteenth century came in 1869 when the 10th Hussars returned from active duty in India and brought with them the sport of polo. Enthusiasm for the new sport on British soil was hampered by the fact that those ponies fulfilling the polo requirements of weight-carrying capacity, size, speed and agility tended to be of cross-bred 'trapper' type, bred specifically for harness work with rather straight shoulders and unsuitable gaits. Some Connemara ponies were bought to train as polo ponies but, when the fashion for larger ponies came in, the market turned to part-bred Arabs and Thoroughbreds as the height limit for polo ponies was repeatedly raised then finally abolished altogether. By the time the Riding and Polo Pony Society (later to become the National Pony Society) was formed in 1893, only two pony breeds, the New Forest and Shetland, had breed societies, and in 1898 the Riding and Polo Pony Society opened sections in Volume V of its stud book for native ponies deemed suitable for crossing with small Thoroughbreds to breed polo ponies. The breeds included at that time were the Dartmoor, Exmoor, Fell (also known as the Brough Hill pony after the main clearance sale for the breed), New Forest, North Wales and South Wales ponies (these were amalgamated from Volume VII of the stud book onwards), and the Scotch (Highland). The Connemara was first included in Volume VI, and the Dales joined in Volume XV soon after the end of the First World War. Regional inspection committees were responsible for drawing up breed standards and passing ponies of correct type for registration, although the chairman of the editing committee added his own criteria in terms of 'the power of the animal to live and thrive in the winter time without any adventitious sustenance'. In other words, acceptance for registration on the basis of appearance alone should not be at the cost of hardiness or native character. Breed conservationists have unfairly criticized the National Pony Society for arbitrarily recognizing some breeds and ignoring others which became extinct, but at that time the Society was not concerned with conserving *breeds* but promoting the breeding of riding and polo ponies. Despite its intentions, the number of native mares used for producing potential polo ponies was relatively small (although the Duchy Tor Royal stud in Devon, founded in 1916 by the Prince of Wales, later King Edward VIII, did use selected Dartmoor mares in the breeding of polo ponies). Instead, the real benefit of the initiative was the recognition given to British pony breeds and the raised awareness of the individuality and uniqueness of the breeds, which led to the formation of other breed societies in years to follow.

NOTES ON SPECIFIC BREEDS AND REGIONS

While one, or a combination, of the factors already mentioned is likely to have had some impact on many of the British Breeds, there are some for whom certain aspects of circumstance and/or location have had specific effects.

Extinct Welsh Breeds

Sir R. D. Green Price, writing in the *Livestock Journal* in November 1891, reported two breeds that are now extinct, although they were in all probability strains of the Welsh pony. The first came from Llanstyd in Breconshire and was spotted and piebald, a colour that Lady Wentworth claimed was an original Welsh colour put out of favour by fashion. Other writers wrote of Breconshire ponies displaying black spots, and spotted colouration was certainly not unknown in some early pony types. Some high-ranking Roman officers purportedly rode spotted animals, although these could have been imported to Britain, rather than native, and there are references to animals with this coat pattern in early illustrated manuscripts. More recently, the famous racehorse, The Tetrarch, displayed some dark spots in his colouration.

The second breed hailed from around Knighton in Powys and was described as mouse-coloured or cream with a black stripe down the back and wall eyes, although greys were also known. While the existence of these cannot be verified, the once-famous Merlins of Wales certainly existed and, before they were absorbed into the Welsh pony, their fame had spread far and wide. The Merlin strain can be traced to the 1740s when an Act passed during the reign of George II banned ponies from racing, resulting in the Williams-Wynn family buying a Thoroughbred pony stallion called Merlin, a descendant of the Darley Arabian, who had broken down on the racecourse. He was turned out on the hills of Denbighshire where, contrary to all expectations, he not only survived but founded a dynasty of superior ponies that eventually bore his name. It was said that 'the stock of his district showed such marked superiority over that from other parts of the country that the value of the young ponies greatly increased', and an issue of the *Sporting Magazine* of 1812 carried a report which stated: 'The small Welsh Merlins are a spirited pigmy race still occupying some hilly walks in the interior of the principality.' An article in the *Cambrian Quarterly Magazine* around 1820 referring to Welsh ponies in the late seventeenth and early eighteenth centuries specifically mentions 'merlyns'. Another Welsh sub-type was found in the Eppynt hills in Breconshire and was said to be dark brown or bay in colour although 'sometimes a grey mare and foal might be seen amongst them, their distinguishing feature being the dark eel-stripe down their backs'.

Scottish Island Breeds

The three main island groups around the Scottish coast are the Shetlands, the Orkneys and the Western Isles, or Inner and Outer Hebrides. Despite their remoteness and harsh terrain, all have supported native pony populations for millennia. The Shetland pony is the best known of the breeds and types associated with these regions, and the impact on the breed of the former demands of the mining industry has been recorded elsewhere in these pages. Of particular interest in the context of lost breeds is the fact that, over the years, the Shetland has given rise to two off-shoots. A type known as the Sumburgh, named after an Iron Age settlement site in the islands, was produced in the mid-nineteenth century by crossing Shetland mares with Norwegian stallions introduced into Dunrossness, the aim being to produce bigger stock for all types of work. The Sumburgh, which could stand up to 13.2 hands (137 cm), was still extant in 1903 when Sir Walter Gilbey wrote about it, but it has now disappeared. A similarly short-lived Shetland offshoot, known as the Fetlar, was produced around the same time through the introduction into the Shetland Islands of a Mustang stallion called Bolivar, but the cross-bred ponies were said to be 'remarkably handsome, swift, spirited but less tractable than the pure Shetland'.

In the Orkneys there was a diminutive breed, of which a traveller in 1703 wrote: 'These horses are of very small size, but hardy, and exposed to the rigour of the season during the winter and spring': this was one of many breeds that eventually succumbed to cross-breeding. The ponies of Lewis, the northernmost of the Western Isles, were also quite small, being described in 1836, as: 'not much higher than Shetland ponies…firm and strong, fit for the mossy soil and rocky shore'. (A breeder from that island sent four of them to King George IV as a present.) At the same time, the general run of Hebridean ponies, which were 'active and remarkably durable and hardy' were reported as being larger, up to 13. 2 hands (137 cm) in some cases – although this size may, even at that time, have been a result of cross-breeding. It is known, for example, that Spanish blood had been introduced to South Uist by the Chief of Clanranald in 1712. There certainly seems to have been an increase in size by the time of the 1836 report as compared to 1695 when, according to Martin in his *Description of the Western Islands of Scotland*, 'the horses are considerably less here than in the opposite continent, yet they plough and harrow as well as bigger horses, though in the spring-time they have nothing to feed upon but sea-ware'.

It has been established that the islands of Mull, Uist, Skye, Barra, Rhum, Staffa, Tiree, Lewis, Harris, Islay, Arran and Eriskay all had their own types of ponies at one time, virtually all of which have gone in the last century and a half (although, as explained in Chapter 6, efforts are being made to save the Eriskay pony). Mull actually had two types, ponies of Galloway type and ponies of a type known as the Gocan or small island pony, of which a writer of 1695 said: 'The horses are but of a low size, yet very sprightly'. The name 'Gocan' is derived from the Gaelic and refers to the breed's small size and great spirit, one pony belonging to Mull's Inspector of Poor carrying his 14 st (89 kg) rider 40 miles (64 km) in a day and then undertaking a further 28 miles (45 km) with a boy in the saddle. The island of Tiree was also home to the Gocan in large numbers and, according to James Macdonald, author of *A General View of the Agriculture of the Hebrides*, published in 1811, 'The island of Tiree keeps 1,500 ponies or nearly as many as the great Isle of Skye, which is twenty times its superficial extent, at least ten times its value, and maintains nearly seven times its population.' The introduction of a Clydesdale stallion to Tiree in the 1870s sounded the death knell for the breed and the Gocan died out around 1900.

Cross-breeding had its influences elsewhere in the Western Isles. As early as 1638 Duncan Campbell, writing to his brother from the island of Islay where many ponies were once bred, said: 'I wyshe if you may Cromarties old Spanish horse provyding he be of a reasonable prys', implying the use of 'improving' stallions as early as the seventeenth century. However, most Western Island types remained virtually unchanged until the early nineteenth century, when the sceptre of cross-breeding to 'improve' the local ponies saw Clydesdale stallions taken to some islands, while Arab stallions were taken to others, including Barra, Harris and Mull, and a roadster stallion was used on the Arran ponies at one point. The indiscrim-inate use of Arabs on Highland ponies of Western Island type produced stock unable to stand the rigours of the islands, as Christopher Wilson observed: 'The Arab crosses will not stand the winter out of doors. I saw a lot of them in the island of Harris, but they could not remain out in winter.'

However, Highland stallions were also introduced to the islands and, among those from the mainland and from Mull which travelled in Skye, probably the most influential was a dappled grey pony called Macneil's Canna whose grandson, Herd Laddie, was to figure so prominently in the history of the Highland pony. Macneil's Canna's background was unusual, for he was out of a black Highland pony mare called Polly whose sire,

Duncan, was a brown Galloway from the island of Mull, and his paternal grandfather was a 15 hands (152.5 cm) brown American stallion called Yankee, owned by the Duke of Argyll's Factor in the Ross of Mull and said to have been brought from the States by the Factor's brother, who was captain of a sailing ship. Writing primarily about Highland ponies in 1937, the Duke of Atholl made an observation about the ponies of the Western Isles and the effects of cross-breeding in general: 'On the islands we find the breed smaller and faster and possibly nearer the original type; smaller, partly on account of the size of the original stock and partly from underfeeding…the best of them have also been subject to less crossing than those of the mainland'.

Following the earlier eighteenth-century infusion of Spanish blood to South Uist, during the latter part of the nineteenth century Arab stallions were introduced to the islands and, in 1872, a contractor from Ayrshire, brought over to build the new school house, brought with him a 15.2 hands (157.5 cm) Clydesdale stallion. Furthermore, in 1890 two Norwegian stallions joined the mix. When improved roads on the island of Barra made the use of wheeled vehicles feasible, the crofters, who originally used their ponies for carrying creels of peat or seaweed, found they needed larger ponies for the vehicles and crossed their Barra ponies with the larger 'improved' Uist ponies 'with the result that the native breed is now almost extinct, or has been crossed with larger sires sent by the Department of Agriculture for Scotland', according to one observer. Similarly, those crofters settled on larger farms in the Western Isles, with more land under tillage, found they needed larger animals to undertake the work and they had also long-since realized that the value of a pony generally increases in direct proportion to its height. In this case, however, The Department of Agriculture for Scotland, (which superseded the Congested Districts Board) began supplying larger sires of a stronger type but without losing the hardy native characteristics, and the risk of irrevocably damaging the breed was purportedly, but questionably, avoided. A similar situation prevailed at the time on the west coast of Ireland.

At one time there was purportedly a white-maned breed on Uist, said

A representative of the now extinct Barra pony, one of the Western Islands' strains of Highland pony, used by the crofters for general agricultural work including carrying creels of peat and seaweed.

to be similar to ponies once found on the Faroe Islands – although there is no evidence of this characteristic in present-day Faroe ponies. However, the dun Fjord pony of Norway does have a pale-coloured mane with the dark eel-stripe running through it and Scandinavian settlers probably introduced Fjord-type ponies to Uist in the ninth century. The original Hebridean ponies were often of a dark brown colour with a lighter muzzle like an Exmoor, although the 'improved' ponies encompassed a wider range of colours. There were also evidently ponies on St. Kilda, although these were brought from another island during the seventeenth century and described as: 'all of red colour, very low and smooth skinned': other, smaller islands probably had imported pony populations too.

The Western Island ponies were sold at special sales and fairs held on the islands, which attracted many of the big dealers from the mainland who virtually monopolized the market and dictated the prices paid, like a buyers' ring at a present-day cattle auction. Some of the dealers who attended to buy strings of ponies came from Aberdeenshire or the south, but they only bought what they could make the most money from and, as larger ponies were more marketable, the dealers did much to encourage the cross-breeding that saw the decline of many of the old island types. It is recorded that in 1783 an average price for a Barra island pony was £2. On Skye there were four annual fairs held between May and November, and other islands had similar gatherings when droves of loose-headed ponies were brought down from the uplands for appraisal and sale to the highest bidder before being shipped to the mainland. In Uist, the ponies were sold at public auctions organized by auction firms from the mainland, whose staff travelled around the islands, having advertised their sales on the mainland first. Once bought and paid for, the dealers haltered their unbroken purchases with the help of some of the crofters, then around six at a time would be tied head to tail with the leader secured to the tail of a strong and steady horse. As one observer noted: 'It was a wonder to me that the tail of this leading horse, with six sturdy colts pulling wildly on it, did not come out of joint.' In this manner the dealer partially tamed his purchases while leading them to the nearest port for shipment to the mainland to start their working lives. One islander, who farmed the now uninhabited island of Vatersay in the 1890s, was reported as wintering as many as forty Barra ponies every year on land where they were fed nothing but what they could graze. Each spring the ponies, which were described as having small Arab-looking heads, were sold to two men who shipped them to Glasgow before exporting them to America.

Today, only the ponies of Rhum and Eriskay are left of all the Western Island ponies although DNA testing has, not surprisingly, shown little genetic difference between these Western Island types and the mainland Highland, despite the fact that the Eriskay has been hailed as a separate breed by its supporters. In his *Journey to the Western Isles* written in 1773, Dr. Samuel Johnson, who was a big and heavy man, complained about the small size of the island ponies but said of those of Rhum: 'The ponies are very small but of a breed eminent for beauty.' Lord Arthur Cecil who, in 1888, sent a number of them down to improve the New Forest breed said: 'The Rhum ponies, which were much thought of by my father, seem to be quite a type of themselves, having characteristics which would almost enable one to recognize them anywhere. Every one of those I bought in 1888 had hazel not brown eyes.' This is a characteristic which persists to this day and they are still remarkable for their distinct colours, many being dark liver chestnut, or golden, or cream dun with darker points and silvery manes and tails, although there were evidently blacks too, once known as

Highland ponies from the Western Island of Rhum always have hazel-coloured eyes, and this unusual feature can occasionally be seen in mainland ponies carrying Rhum blood.

Black Galloways. According to an article in *The Times* in April 1957 there were twenty-two ponies left on Rhum and they were described as 'small and sturdy'. In recent years, the Rhum ponies have shown some deterioration, a trend emphasized by comparison with the consistent improvement of the mainland type of Highland, and Rhum ponies are now registered in the main section of the Highland Pony Society stud book, although Eriskays have a society of their own overseeing their registrations.

It is a sobering thought that breeds which had taken centuries to develop could be lost within the span of a few decades, and yet so many were. When utility dictated the market, and terms like genetic diversity were as totally alien to horse and pony breeders as the concept of pure breeds, the losses went unnoticed. Once allowed to slip into extinction, breeds cannot be recreated and although some look-alikes have been produced which are similar in appearance they are genetically far removed from the original, which is gone forever.

Chapter 8

THE FUTURE FOR BRITISH BREEDS

I do daily find in mine experience, that the virtue, goodness, boldness, swiftness, and endurance of our true-bred English horses is equal with any race of horses whatsoever.
Gervaise Markham, 1607

CURRENT THREATS

There is a bitter irony to the fact that, after centuries of gradual evolution into distinct and unique breeds, and having survived hunting, persecution, loss of habitat and the demise of horsepower as a motive force, with the coming of recognition, value, popularity and increasing registration numbers, many British horse and pony breeds are probably in greater danger of extinction now than ever before.

It would be naïve to think that breeds are static, for development is ongoing and there is a trend that has seen virtually all British breeds change more in the last century than in the preceding many hundreds of years, but this forces us to consider in which direction the future of these breeds lies and what we may have left in another hundred years, or even less. The changing demands of today's agricultural economy, coupled with the fact that there are no laws in Britain to protect rare breeds of farm livestock (including the working horse breeds), puts all minority breeds at risk – although it is encouraging to know that, since the Rare Breeds Survival Trust was formed in 1973, no British breeds have slipped into extinction. However, there is no room for complacency.

For some breeds the threat lies in low breeding stock numbers. A survey undertaken a few years ago showed that there were between 1,100 and 1,200 pure-bred Exmoor ponies in the world but of those only 80 stallions and 388 mares could be classed as breeding stock, making the breed considerably rarer than many wild species classed as endangered. The Rare Breeds Survival Trust employs a scale of rarity based on the number of registered breeding females: Mainstream being over 3,000; Minority being under 3,000; At Risk under 1,500; Vulnerable less than 900; Endangered less than 500; and Critical less than 300. At the time of writing, Cleveland Bays, Suffolks, Dales and Eriskay ponies are all on the Critical list, with Exmoor ponies and Hackney horses and ponies on the Endangered list, and Dartmoors, Clydesdales and semi-feral Welsh Section A ponies classed as Vulnerable, leaving Fell ponies, Highlands and Shire horses deemed to be At Risk. The other breeds are Mainstream, with safe breeding numbers. Put into context, many British breeds are actually rarer than the Giant Panda.

Low breeding numbers can significantly reduce the gene pool in a breed, causing a bottleneck like that which occurred around 1960 when the Cleveland Bay was in crisis and one council member of the time noted: 'I think it true to say we were down to three, possibly four, mature Cleveland stallions in this entire hemisphere. One of those was very old and just about related to everything.' Aware of the breed's plight, in 1962, H. M. The Queen, whose grandfather had bred Cleveland Bays back in the 1920s, purchased the yearling colt, Mulgrave Supreme, to prevent his impending export to the United States and to make his bloodline available to British breeders by standing him at public stud, an action which heralded a turning point in the Cleveland Bay's fortunes. Similar bottlenecks have occurred elsewhere: in 1914 the five stallions awarded premiums by the Fell Pony

Society were all direct descendants of a famous pony called Blooming Heather, and as late as 1979 the eighteen Highland pony stallions awarded premiums by their breed society traced back on one or both sides to a famous and influential stallion called Herd Laddie. Other breeds have also shown evidence of severely reduced gene pools at various times in their history owing to the popularity or pre-potency of individual stallions (a factor explored below).

In 2000, the Rare Breeds Survival Trust published the results of a study looking at the levels of homozygosity (animals inheriting the same alleles from each of their parents) in rare equines. In an inbred population, levels of homozygosity tend to increase as there are fewer possible variants left in the gene pool. A high level of heterozygosity (animals inheriting different genes from each parent) indicates a greater variety of alleles present in the population. This can be used to measure the genetic health of a breed. The heterozygosity of a sample of British rare breed ponies (Fell, Dales, Eriskays and Dartmoors) was 54%, with the Exmoor at 47% – which the researchers found alarming, although perhaps not surprising, considering there were only fifty Exmoors left in 1945.

With increased mobility in terms of equine transport and access to more stallions over a greater geographical spread, a new cause of shrinking genetic diversity has now arisen as breeders tend to use those stallions which breed well and produce show-ring prize-winners, which quickly reduces the available bloodlines within a breed. This problem can be evidenced by scanning through the various stud books and noting the diversity of bloodlines. A software programme called SPARKS (the Single Population Analysis and Record Keeping System), which was developed to help widen the gene pools of endangered wildlife in captive zoo breeding projects, has been used to track the inter-related world population of pure-bred Cleveland Bays, and other systems have been used in other breeds for similar purposes. In all such cases the aim is to avoid mixing rare bloodlines, maximize the genetic diversity of the whole population, and reduce the level of inbreeding.

In the past, inbreeding was often prevented by occasional outcrosses to another breed, something that was commonplace before the formation of breed societies and frequently but more discreetly done after many societies came into existence. Over the years, innumerable experiments were made to improve one native breed by introducing the blood of another and, because of the common ancestry at some point in the history of most breeds, this was often successful in at least preventing genetic bottlenecks. The Fell and Dales breeds were much interlinked until comparatively recently, similar links existed at one time between the Shire and Clydesdale horses, and the New Forest breed has seen a succession of stallions of other breeds turned out on the forest, to mention just a few. Individual breeders, openly or clandestinely, have often dabbled with different crosses and most of the stud books contain some surprising entries and some even more surprising omissions. The Earl of Ancaster introduced Dales blood into some of his Highland ponies with good results, Highlands were used successfully in the New Forest, and the ponies of Skye were influenced by a Welsh pony stallion who travelled on the island and left a lot of good stock. In the north of England a Welsh Cob stallion was used very successfully in the Fell breed at one time, while a well-known Fell stallion, Linnel Don, sired many prize-winners in Welsh pony classes, but as his breeder, Roy B. Charlton, noted in 1944: 'This only goes to prove that an infusion of real pony blood from one pure mountain breed to another mountain pony breed can produce real ponies...go back far enough in the history of Britain's native ponies, and it will be found that they were all one stock.'

In 1912 the President of the Board of Agriculture and Fisheries formed a committee to consider the improvement of mountain and moorland ponies, and the report produced recommended the interchange of stallions between the native pony breeds with the aim of improving the pony stock in general. Other supporters of British breeds were vehemently against any form of cross-breeding, including Major Jack Fairfax-Blakeborough, a former Secretary of the Cleveland Bay Horse Society, whose response to the suggestion that Hackney blood might improve the Cleveland was: 'I consider they (Hackneys) have evolved into an abomination before the Lord. This unnatural snap they talk so much about only appeals to retired publicans and pork butchers who want to drive four miles or so and home again. Breeding such a useless type should be made a penal offence.' Supporters of other breeds were more receptive to the idea, although the results were certainly not always a success.

RELATIONSHIP OF TYPE TO ENVIRONMENT

Some breeds can boast a large breeding population which should, in theory, guarantee survival. However, if breed type is subconsciously lost as the breed gradually metamorphosizes into something different over time, or the breed standard is compromised to accommodate fashions, especially in judging and show-ring preferences, then we have lost the breed without actually realizing it and this must now be a real and major threat to survival across many breeds. By looking at photographs of breed champions from the past at intervals of around twenty-five years, it is soon apparent that many of the top-class horses and ponies of a century ago would be unlikely to win a prize in the show-ring today, which questions whether we have improved these breeds in the intervening years or, in reality, moved away from the true type and created something different, like the 'new and improved breeds' produced at the expense or the extinction of others, which Sir Walter Gilbey wrote about over a century ago. Has the modern Shire Horse the working capacity, strength and stamina of its forebears or, in improving its appearance and action, has some utilitarian element been lost? Similarly, could some of the Section B Welsh ponies of riding type bred today survive a harsh winter on the Welsh hills and, if not, at what stage in their recent history did they come to the point when they could no longer be classed as mountain and moorland ponies. To purists, a true mountain and moorland pony is one whose ancestors have lived on mountain, moor or common for the last three generations in semi-feral conditions – although there are relatively few ponies now which could meet those criteria and there is a danger that, apart from a few token free-living ponies, eventually there may actually be none.

By looking at a typical representative of a particular breed, its appearance should indicate its origins, the environment which moulded its characteristics, and the work it was used for. Everything about the modern Thoroughbred would suggest oriental ancestry and speed, and its physical features indicate the breeding environment of its ancestors and a somewhat cosseted evolution on English soil, as this breed was developed primarily for racing but sometimes at a cost of inherent soundness and an equable temperament. A native pony, on the other hand, is a complex product of its environment with a plethora of physical features designed to help it cope with its surroundings, including a weather-resistant coat with vortices (changes in the direction in which the hair lies) designed to channel away rain, a chute tail for shedding water, hard and resilient hooves to cope with rocky ground, and well-developed teeth and jaws for grazing on the roughest terrain. In addition to these visible features, there are equally important invisible qualities like hardiness, stamina, vigour, self-reliance, sure-footedness and instinct that were vital to the survival of these breeds and which have been acquired over a long period, but which can be lost within a few generations if no longer needed as the evolutionary process soon discards what it does not need. Thomas Pennant, the scientist who toured the Hebridean islands in 1773, made use of the local indigenous ponies for both riding and pack work and noted in his journals the cautious way they traversed the peat bogs and rocky slopes, using the instincts and knowledge developed by living in that environment. Once native ponies are kept on better ground in a milder climate, hand-fed, stabled or rugged, and generally given a softer lifestyle, the attributes of survival will soon begin to fade. The invisible qualities will only be retained by working the animals in appropriate occupational fields so these attributes are called upon and, if possible, by allowing them to live and breed in an environment as close as possible to that in which they evolved. For this reason, breeders, especially those from outside Britain, need to go back to source periodically to retain that important link and preserve those unique characteristics and inherent skills. Speaking of Welsh Mountain ponies, the Secretary of the Welsh Hill Improvement Societies warned: 'Without the hill pony, lowland breeders will be unable to replenish the Section A's hardiness.'

For centuries, Nature's survival of the fittest regime saw only the strongest and most resourceful animals live to breed and perpetuate the species, a sometimes brutal but natural system which, in bad winters like that of 1946–47, saw most pure-bred native ponies survive the extreme weather while cross-bred ponies running out with them often perished. That winter was so severe that all but one of a group of Fell ponies cut off by deep snow in a Cumbrian valley for nine weeks perished, the sole survivor being the stallion, Heltondale Romer, who lived on to leave his mark on the breed. Nowadays, with the larger part of the native pony population kept in conditions where supplementary feeding, shelter in adverse weather and other comforts have taken Nature out of the equation, all ponies will theoretically survive and the element of natural selection is taken away, with potentially serious long-term consequences. Rigorous inspections and veterinary examinations, especially for stallions, undoubtedly help to protect 'type', but these only cover visible attributes and characteristics, not the unseen attributes which Nature would test in the wild, and assessing survival skills in a domestic situation is difficult, if not approaching impossible. If ponies could be kept in conditions similar to their native environment for at least part of their life, perhaps as young stock, some indicators might be picked up which would provide information of their suitability as future breeding stock. Considering that the breeding stock, stallions and mares, of a whole population is not a high percentage, those animals failing to meet the criteria for breeding could be absorbed into the ranks of riding and driving ponies, fulfilling useful roles but not passing on weaker genes.

Beyond simply substituting their naturally harsh terrain with lowland pasture, many well-intentioned but often inexperienced pony owners are frequently guilty of actually over-pampering their animals, which further negates the need for survival skills. In the wild or in semi-feral herds, ponies follow a natural cycle whereby they can lose up to one-third of their body weight over the winter and, with the coming of the spring grass, put weight on again over the summer months ready for the following winter. Those that are 'bad doers' and fail to follow this seasonal cycle are more likely not to survive the winter to breed the following year. However, as most domestic owners do not like to see their ponies lean at the end of the winter or over-fat towards the end of a good summer, their condition is managed. Although this is understandable in such contexts as concern for the well-being of an older animal that loses condition too readily, the practice of keeping animals – especially young stock – too fat, as they often are for the show ring, can be detrimental.

In the wild, ponies tend to avoid grazing dunging sites, minimizing worm infestation, and they build up a resistance to internal parasites that is compromised when they are kept in small paddocks. Some ponies and horses have been observed selectively nibbling poisonous plants including yew, broom and the young and carcinogenic fronds of bracken, which may possibly be a natural worming dose. In the interests of responsible management most owners, even of semi-feral ponies, consider worming to be mandatory and humane, like the provision of supplementary feeding in harsh weather, yet free-living ponies will often shun hay or other feed in winter if natural alternatives like gorse are available. However, knowing what to eat and where to find it in harsh weather is a skill partly inherent and partly learnt from older herd animals and practised through need, and if the need is taken away the skills will be lost, so maintaining an understanding of survival skills is essential if there is any hope of seeing free-living herds of native ponies in the future.

Conservationists have long since realized that the key to conserving any species is to ensure that its natural environment is protected. Greater demands on the finite land resources which were once the natural terrain of many pony breeds has resulted in relatively small numbers of ponies still accurately defined as free-living in their original habitat. Both horses and ponies are very successful at adapting to easier conditions and it is a concern that, if moved from the environments which helped create our breeds, they will adapt to their new terrain relatively quickly, and change. A problem that Connemara breeders have experienced is that when fed on better land in milder climates, the ponies tend to grow bigger and lose type, unlike the Shetland which gets fat but stays the same size. This may be attributable to the Connemara's mixed ancestry, with the result that an element of undesirable hybrid vigour manifests itself in favourable conditions and they breed less true to type.

Other reasons for decreasing numbers of native ponies bred under natural conditions on upland grazing or common ground include fewer breeders with access to hill grazing, changes in hill farming practices, less interest from younger generations in maintaining the hill herds, and poor financial returns on the breeding and selling of foals. When the Land Enclosures Acts were passed around two hundred years ago, permitting the fencing and subsequent private ownership of large tracts of open land, agrarian communities fought to hang on to their communal grazing rights which date back to the medieval manorial system. The Commons Registration Act of 1965 confirmed farmers' rights to graze stock on unenclosed commons, but even for those with some guaranteed tenure the financial and time resource costs in rearing, registering and getting passports for ponies can often outweigh the return, especially for colt foals. In 1997, out of a total of 290 Fell pony foals registered, 115 were bred from hill-roaming stock, but by 2000 only 91 foals out of 272 were hill foals.

On Exmoor, the National Park Authority runs some ponies on the moor, a practice which provides more continuity than can be guaranteed with private ownership and helps with the natural maintenance of the moor, and similar schemes have been tried successfully elsewhere. Back in 1932 the National Trust was persuaded to establish a small select stud of Fell ponies when the breed was at risk, so that a nucleus of pure-bred ponies would survive whatever else happened and, although it was not the Trust's policy to keep livestock, they maintained the herd until 1950. In Scotland, where there were at one time many free-roaming herds of Highland ponies, there is now only one herd of around eighteen ponies left and that is on the Hebridean island of Rhum, which is owned and managed as a nature reserve by Scottish Natural Heritage. Before The Nature Conservancy (now Scottish National Heritage) bought Rhum in 1957, successive previous owners had maintained the old Rhum bloodlines and never introduced female blood from outside. Until comparatively recently, the Highland Pony Society has generally seemed to take limited interest in these ponies, which are essentially working animals used as deer ponies on the island, but a greater awareness of the importance of semi-feral ponies to breeds and the importance of genetic diversity in the gene pool has brought them into focus again, with constructive discussion between Scottish National Heritage and Highland Pony Society members.

COMPETITION WITH AGRICULTURAL LIVESTOCK, AND CONSERVATION INITIATIVES

Another issue for free-roaming herds is competition with other agricultural hill stock and the impact of stocking levels on the environment. For farmers with a legal right to graze stock including ponies on common land, the Department for the Environment, Food and Rural Affairs (Defra), who designate some uplands as Environmentally Sensitive Areas (ESAs) to preserve the natural environment, also set a maximum stocking level in terms of 'livestock units'. A unit can be a horse or a bovine over six months of age, while a pony counts as 0.6 of a unit, and a ewe with lambs 0.15 of a unit. In the north-west of England, where reducing numbers of Fell ponies still roam some of the highest common upland grazing, the Commoners' Associations of the individual fells or uplands decide how the total units are made up and pony-breeding Commoners are usually in a minority. Compensation of around £100 per pony per annum to take them off encourages many breeders to do so. Although participation in a management scheme is not compulsory and a Commoner with rights can still turn ponies out, they rarely do so, as pressure from other Commoners is strong. Defra does not consider the historical significance of the role of the terrain in moulding the breed, nor does it take into account the different grazing preferences of ponies, sheep and cattle, the latter two having to be removed from the uplands for winter months while the ponies can remain. Stocking levels of mixed stock have a direct impact on the range of grazing plants available as much as the actual quantity of food, compelling ponies to change their natural diets to survive. Over-grazing causes deterioration in the vegetation, while recreational use of moorlands by off-road motorists and motorcycles (and to a lesser extent the use of quad bikes by farmers to check their stock) can also damage grasses, although some management of

Fell ponies grazing in their natural environment. Decreasing numbers of native ponies are now kept and bred on common ground or uplands because of changes in farming practices and because fewer breeders have access to such grazing.

moorland by burning old woody gorse and heather (which encourages nutritious new growth) can greatly improve its grazing potential. Because the ponies eat hay and feed put out for cattle and sheep, they are generally disliked by the farmers yet, if agreement can be reached between the various parties, the benefits of allowing young stock to be kept on common grazing to instil natural instincts outweigh the negatives.

By comparison with the above, the use of ponies in conservation grazing elsewhere has made significant advances in recent years. With the reform of the European Common Agricultural Policy and the phasing out of subsidies linked to production (which in many cases encouraged the over-grazing of uplands), the implications for these traditional grazing areas, which constitute one quarter of Britain, are great. In short, upland landscapes could change completely, with ramifications for both the local fauna and flora. Having evolved to survive on poor grazing, native ponies are resourceful and adaptable in their diet and this can be of great benefit in certain situations where they may control scrub encroachment and the proliferation of some dominant woody species. A study of Exmoor ponies revealed that grass species constituted only 58 per cent of their diet over the year, ranging from 75 per cent in summer to 31 per cent in winter when the grasses had their lowest nutritional value. Heather made up another 10 per cent of the diet, followed by gorse at 9 per cent and rushes at 8 per cent. The remaining 15 per cent of the diet was not clearly identified, but a similar study of New Forest ponies revealed significant quantities of mosses eaten, while bracken, which is poisonous when the fronds are unfurling, was also eaten but only in small quantities. Studies of other breeds have shown that browsing on shrubs and the low-hanging branches of trees makes up an appreciable part of the diet in the summer months, while the importance of gorse, which has a high nutritional value and is available all year round, is common to all breeds with access to it. Many native ponies acquire the skill of pawing at gorse bushes with their forefeet to bruise and soften the prickles to make it easier to eat, and some develop a protective moustache to facilitate the eating of gorse, thistle flowers and holly leaves.

The use of native ponies in conservation grazing projects has made significant advances in recent years and contributed to maintaining the upland grazing areas which constitute one quarter of Britain.

The historical relationship between wild-living ponies and their environment is one of mutual survival, the ponies having evolved in balance with their environment and, by eating the coarse grasses which would otherwise overwhelm other plant species and by controlling the gorse through eating it in winter when other fare is scarce, they maintain the natural vegetation. This trait has been put to good use by the National Trust, English Heritage, the Corporation of London and other bodies with areas of natural landscape to manage and conserve. At the National Trust's coastal heather reserve on the Purbecks in Dorset, Exmoor ponies were used to graze the invasive tor grass down to a short sward, enabling the rare early spider orchid to compete with the grass and thrive. As the Head Warden explained: 'Ponies were chosen by virtue of the fact that they can live on very poor areas and they tend to eat the scrub and grasses less favourable to sheep and cattle. They also require very little management time.' Elsewhere Shetland ponies, Dartmoors, New Forests and other breeds have been used successfully for conservation grazing.

As the restoration and conservation of areas of natural habitat for wildlife become increasingly important issues, conservation grazing could also play a vital role in the preservation of native ponies by providing an opportunity for at least a nucleus of breeding stock to be kept in their natural environment, helping to safeguard the invisible qualities that could otherwise be lost. Defra offers financial incentives to farmers to ensure that Environmentally Sensitive Areas, including heather moorland, are neither under- nor over-grazed, which could either cause problems for breeders or provide conservation grazing opportunities depending on the circumstances. The Country Stewardship Scheme is designed to protect upland Sites of Special Scientific Interest (SSSIs), and English Nature is keen to graze such areas with traditional breeds of cattle, sheep and ponies in the belief that their grazing patterns will best support biodiversity. Evidence has shown that Exmoor and Welsh Mountain ponies in particular graze selectively, avoiding heather (which sheep do eat) when other favoured vegetation is available, and producing diverse mosaics of vegetation that favour invertebrates, small mammals and birds of prey while allowing rare plant species to thrive and flower. English Nature's Traditional Breeds Incentive lists native pony breeds as the priority breeds to help maintain heather landscapes, and perhaps this theme could be developed further, with more upland grazing being made available to breeders of native ponies where their young stock could run out for the summer months for a nominal fee so that the ponies could spent at least part of their formative years in their natural environment.

The breeding of native ponies on their natural terrain would, of course, be greatly encouraged if financial incentives for breeders, perhaps in the form of government subsidies, could be made available with the aim of promoting the 'green' agenda and conserving part of the undervalued British national heritage, which also has considerable tourism potential. As early as 1901 a writer in the *Scottish Farmer* suggested that if a supply of tough, handy ponies was to be made available for army remounts, then consideration should be given to maintaining breeding herds on cheap marginal grazing in a climate that made hand-feeding superfluous. 'Grazing among rocks and bogs makes the animals active, sure-footed and clever in extricating themselves from tight places, a very essential thing for mounted cavalry', he added, acknowledging both the value of native pony types and the benefits of subsidized breeding enclosures where animals are raised in a natural environment. In 1988 a scheme was initiated in the Dartmoor National Park to encourage the breeding of the true Dartmoor pony on its native heath, with support from the Duchy of Cornwall, the National Parks Authority and the Ministry of Agriculture. The Dartmoor Pony Society Moor Scheme, as it is called, is essentially a breeding enclosure, not dissimilar to those run by other breed societies at various times with great success, but it provides the additional benefit of allowing the general public to see ponies in their natural environment, which has added considerable publicity value. Despite this local success, a nationwide scheme to encourage and promote the breeding of registered native ponies in free-living herds as a long-term strategy would achieve much.

USES OF OFFICIAL FUNDING

The Horserace Betting Levy Board has offered tremendous support to the British horse industry continuously since 1950, but since the late 1990s it has focused its breed society funding on rare breeds, contributing significantly to the work of struggling breed societies who, in 2007, received a total grant of £172,000. The Board has a list of approved purposes for which the funds may be used and these include stallion, mare and foal premiums, travel grants (for example, to allow mares to be covered by a premium stallion), DNA testing, microchipping, and mountain and moorland schemes. It is up to the breed societies how they allocate the grant within the approved purposes, most tending to focus on premiums, although DNA testing and microchipping are becoming more common. Breed societies can also propose other uses for the grant which they believe to be appropriate and the Board will approve these if they are considered beneficial to the breed. As these breed societies already administer premiums for breeding stock, they would be best placed to administer government subsidies (if they could be made available) to ensure they achieved what was intended and, in the promotion of free-living herds, did not unwittingly encourage breed division into semi-feral and domesticated ponies. At a time when traditional skills in rural communities are receiving recognition and support, the unique skills of the hill farmers/breeders, handed down from generation to generation, in managing semi-feral herds should also not be undervalued for, once lost, these skills are unlikely to be re-learnt.

Including the only non-mountain and moorland pony breed, the Hackney pony, as well as its larger relation, the Hackney horse and also the Cleveland Bay, Irish Draught and the British heavy horse breeds in any government subsidy scheme would, of course, be essential as the aim of any financial incentives must be to conserve *all* recognized British breeds, not just mountain and moorland ponies. Other indirect financial benefits could possibly include exemption for hill ponies or minority horse breeds from the European Union's requirement for all equines over six months of age to have passports, incentives to encourage new breeders under the farm diversification banner, and marketing initiatives to promote British native breeds as a tourism feature.

THE IMPACT OF SHOWING

As a result of the popularity of showing, appearance in terms of conformation and action is now the primary consideration of most breeders, exhibitors and judges, with breed type secondary, and performance capabilities or the ability to work of least importance. Fortunately, most people consider good temperament to be an essential attribute. In times past, performance was the top priority and, although conformation and action do impact upon capability, they were not the primary consideration, and breed type was just something that took care of itself. The old criteria may now have been turned around completely, but it is important to keep a balance between appearance and performance so that we are not just preserving something that looks good but has no function, like the reproduction lamps on a carriage that cannot be lit. If the breeds we ultimately end up with are a far cry from what they were originally, we may have unwittingly contributed to the deterioration or loss of true breed type without even being aware of it. In planning to safeguard all the qualities of all these breeds, a clear strategy for the future is essential if a standard of excellence and benchmark for conformation, action, breed type and performance capability are to be maintained. Without such a strategy, it is very much a case of, 'If you don't know where you want to go, any road will take you there' – and many British breeds are at a crossroads.

The whims of fashion should have no place in the conservation of horse and pony breeds but, human nature being what it is, fickle and short-term preferences have historically done much harm by encouraging the indiscriminate production of a popular breed to meet demand while other less popular breeds slipped into decline. This is especially noticeable in other countries where the rarity value of certain British breeds has seen animals of indifferent quality and type imported and bred from for immediate financial gain rather than the promotion and furtherance of the breed. However, this is not exclusively a recent trend for, in the late nineteenth century, William Scarth Dixon wrote:

> Perhaps no breed of horses has experienced such vicissitudes as the Cleveland Bay has done during the last century. At one time it would be in the greatest demand; at another it would be practically despised, and a horse bred from the Cleveland Bay, or containing Cleveland Bay blood, was almost unsaleable, was looked upon as soft, and too frequently condemned without trial.

Today, the craving for individuality has seen rarer colours in breeds often gaining popularity on the grounds that people, especially those who show, want something different because it stands out in the show-ring. On a wider and more positive scale, rare breeds of all livestock have made a comeback in recent years, partially owing to the efforts of the Rare Breed Survival Trust and partly owing to an interest among the general public in anything scarce or unusual. The Dales pony, which suffered a ten-year decline up until 2005, has seen an upturn in its fortunes more recently, with foal registrations now standing at around 160 a year and demand exceeding supply for broken ponies.

The people who probably have the greatest influence on trends within breeds are judges, because the popularity of showing in the last fifty years or so has seen show-ring champions becoming the standard breeders aspire to,

The popularity of showing in recent years has brought many breeds, including the Connemara, more into the public eye. However, to be beneficial to the breeds, it is important that correct criteria are applied in the show-ring.

even though this may at times slightly contradict the official breed standard. For example, the standard for the Fell pony says that the feather should be straight and silky and that in summer it may be cast except for a little at the heel, whereas in reality the majority of prize-winners have considerably more feather, as this has become a favoured feature in the show-ring. Judges have supported this trend and breeders have followed it but the breed standard has never been amended to reflect the change.

All the horse and pony breed societies operate some form of judges' selection procedure and maintain a list of judges approved by the respective societies to try to guarantee standards in the show-ring as well as for inspections for registration and other purposes. However, once approved onto a panel, there is rarely any form of appraisal or review of judges, with the result that judges who are, or become, less than competent are difficult to remove from the judges' panels, while interpretation of breed standards remains a perennial and contentious issue. Judges' seminars, open days and instructional events – whether organized by individual breed societies or other bodies – can all do much to maintain high and consistent standards, but anomalies in judging are still commonly reported in the showing columns of the equestrian press and every season produces controversial show-ring decisions. Judging, like the breeds themselves, is not static and the problems generally lie with those judges who tend to operate in isolation, rather than as part of a larger judging community promoting a more consistent standard in judging, and supporting the aims of breed societies in achieving a wider understanding and implementation of an agreed standard of excellence.

Showing in general has a number of drawbacks in addition to the obvious benefit of publicizing and marketing the different breeds. In mixed breed classes, which are more usual for pony rather than horse breeds, the judging criteria should be to select in order of priority those animals which are the best representatives of their breeds. For judges, this necessitates a thorough knowledge of *all* breeds, which is not always apparent, and breeds of great beauty like Dartmoors or those with spectacular action like Welsh

Cobs are often put up over their less flamboyant peers. However, if a breed like the Exmoor is penalized because it has a less refined head than a Welsh Section A, despite the fact that Exmoors have, and have always had, a distinct shape of head for evolutionary reasons, then Shetland ponies might also be penalized because they are small. Only by judging each breed against its own breed standard can consistency in judging be achieved.

The popularity of showing native ponies has also seen a significant change in the way animals are presented in the show-ring, a trend encouraged by professional show pony yards, with many native ponies quite simply 'over-produced' for shows. At one time, ponies were literally brought off grass and taken to the local show with the minimum of attention beforehand. Inevitably, standards of turnout have improved over the years, but the artificial turnout now achieved, especially at winter shows, with the aid of rugging, solariums, special diets, discreet trimming and the apparent pulling of manes and tails, questions the appropriateness of this style of presentation in mountain and moorland classes.

TRENDS IN COLOUR, HEIGHT AND TYPE

For various reasons, most breeds will show *some* trends over the years, although these may be almost imperceptible if introduced gradually. Colour is one of the easiest to pinpoint. Many of the early Highland ponies were black or brown with some duns, often with zebra markings, but Herd Laddie, a grey stallion foaled in 1881, changed that and was responsible for the predominance of greys in the breed today. While duns and creams with an eel-stripe and dark points were always popular, grey was never a favourite colour for deer-stalking ponies as it is too conspicuous. Neither, in fact, did it find favour with the remount officers requisitioning animals of any breed for military use, since it offered little in the way of natural camouflage compared to dark colours, and grooms generally disliked greys because of the extra work needed to turn them out well. However, for the very reasons that greys were unpopular as working ponies, showing has brought them back into favour as they are eye-catching, and grey Highlands, Fells, Dales, Welsh ponies and Connemaras are often particularly sought-after by the showing community. In fact grey is now *the* favoured colour in the Connemara breed, and grey and roan Dales ponies have shown an increase in recent years. Regarding Welsh ponies, as with the Highland, a single stallion seems to have been influential in the emergence of grey as a colour. A photograph of the Longmynd Welsh ponies taken in 1892 shows that the majority of the 1,250 ponies rounded up and driven through the streets of Church Stretton that year were dark-coloured, with relatively few white markings. However, the only grey pony recorded in Volume I of the Welsh Stud Book, a stallion called Dyoll Starlight, foaled in 1894, changed all that by founding a dynasty of outstanding ponies, many of whom inherited his grey colour.

In other breeds, different colours have come into the ascendancy. Historically, bays and browns were the most prevalent colours in the Fell, but black has taken over in popularity, specifically as a show-ring fashion, as black ponies show their condition well. In the Shetland pony, colour preferences have varied over the years. Martin, writing in 1703, said: 'The black are esteemed to be the most hardy, but the pied ones seldom prove to be so good.' More recently, chestnut was the favoured colour but, of late, piebalds and skewbalds have taken over in popularity. The breed standard for the Dartmoor pony used to read: 'Colours: bay, brown, black, grey, chestnut, but no colour bar except piebald and skewbald', implying clear preferences for the first-named colours, but this has now been reworded to include all but part-colours.

Across all breeds the predominance of certain bloodlines, trends and fashions will frequently produce waves of one colour or another, except in the case of the Cleveland Bay, which is always bay, or the Suffolk Punch, which is always chestnut. However, even in the Cleveland Bay, some colour characteristics like the black dorsal stripe, black spots on the body and zebra markings on the forelegs which were once not uncommon in the breed have all but disappeared – although they still occasionally manifest themselves in some individuals. Some oddities of colour can probably be traced to the effects of cross-breeding, for example one noted Highland brood mare was described by John Macdonald as 'a strongly-built mare, cream-coloured with the usual black eel stripe, a rather white blaze on face and two white (well up to the hocks) hind legs. Those markings showed distinct traces of Clydesdale blood.' A number of piebald Highland ponies were bred by John Cameron prior to 1833 but they died out and their unusual colouration was undoubtedly the result of an outcross at some time or other.

Many breeds have seen height increases over the years. For example, the Fell Pony Society raised the height limit for ponies from 13.2 to 14 hands (137 to 142 cm) some years ago, and the Exmoor Pony Society redefined the section referring to height in its breed standard to state a preferred height range of 11.3–12.3 hands (119.4–129.5 cm) for stallions at maturity and 11.2–12.2 hands (117–127 cm) for mares at maturity so as not to exclude ponies outside this height band – while not encouraging them either. The Dales Pony Society did something similar, stating in their revised breed standard that the preferred height for ponies was 14–14.2 hands (142–147.3 cm). Attempts were made in 1957 and 1958 to reduce the 12.2 hands (127 cm) height limit for Dartmoors to 12 hands (122 cm) and 11.3 hands (119.4 cm) respectively but on both occasions the motion was defeated when put to the vote. The Connemara appears to be gradually increasing in size and, like the heavy horse breeds and Cleveland Bay and Irish Draught, the Welsh Section D actually has no upper height limit, although some of the very large individuals lack quality and native character. In other breeds the relevant society has sanctioned the raising of the height limit to meet market demands, which is a worrying trend as the market should not dictate the breed standard when there is sufficient diversity in British breeds to suit all buyers.

It is, however, in breed *type* that the most significant changes within some breeds have been recorded. One possible drawback to the formation of breed societies and the agreeing of breed standards is, almost inevitably, that it discourages diversity of type within breeds and, as a consequence, causes the loss of some of the less fashionable bloodlines. Valuing old bloodlines even if they do not produce show-ring prize winners can contribute to the overall health of a breed. In the National Pony Society stud book for 1945–1947, 25 per cent of the ponies registered as Highlands were of Western Island type, whereas in the Highland Pony Society stud book for 1992 it was only 3.3 per cent – and some of those were geldings. In general, judges see the mainland type of Highland as the accepted model and, with the Highland Pony Society perhaps reluctant at one time to recognize the distinction between the two types, many judges considered ponies of Western Isle type to be short of bone and substance and consequently left them out of the rosettes. By being declared a distinct breed the Eriskay ponies have secured their own classes at shows like the Royal Highland Show, whereas the show-ring potential for Rhum ponies, the only other surviving Western Island type, is currently severely limited.

In referring to many breeds, people often talk about 'old-fashioned type' in relation to bone and substance, but photographic evidence reveals that some breeds (including the Dales) have become more substantial over the years, while other breeds like the Welsh Section B have, in many cases, lost substance. Some breed societies once even recognized two types within their breeds, including the Fell Pony Society which, at one time, ran two breeding enclosures with a stallion of heavier type on one and a stallion of riding type on the other and, in the Cleveland Bay breed, strains of weight-carrying pack horse and faster coaching types were once far more apparent than is the case today.

The popularity of many British breeds internationally brings new concerns for breed societies, especially those with daughter societies in other countries, as it becomes more difficult to ensure compliance with regulations and maintain standards. Within the European Community it has been agreed that the country of origin of a breed maintains the parent stud book and determines the criteria for registration, with the member countries operating daughter stud books under those adopted criteria.

When one considers that there are more Suffolk Punches in North America than England, and that Shetland pony registrations in Holland average 5,000 a year, while those in the United Kingdom stand at around 3,000, the issue of who controls the future of British breeds is clearly put into context. It is all a far cry from the early days of most British breed societies, when the committee members were all local breeders who, in looking after their own interests as breeders, automatically looked after the interests of the breed as the two were synonymous.

Strong characters and dogmatic personal views can often lead to stormy breed society meetings when contentious issues are being discussed, and the controversial subject of whether breed societies should maintain part-bred registers has often been debated with inconsistent outcomes. Interestingly, while the Highland Pony Society averages 350 pure-bred registrations per annum, its part-bred register averages only around ten. Some societies, especially among the horse breeds where the market for 'sport' horses is considerable, feel that by registering part-breds their breed gets credit and publicity, while others feel it encourages cross-breeding and devalues the pure-bred. The waters can be muddied by the fact that some part-breds may be prodigious performers. Foxhunter, the famous show-jumper who won the King George V Cup three times and clinched the gold medal for the British team at the Helsinki Olympics in 1952 was one-quarter Clydesdale, and Nizefella, another outstanding show-jumper of the time, carried Shire blood in his veins – but these horses were bred when the future for pure-bred heavy horses was at its bleakest. Another outstanding jumper, Greatheart, who established the world high-jump record in Chicago in 1920 when he cleared 8 feet 2 inches (2.49 m) was sired by a Hackney, and other Hackney part-breds have proved to have tremendous jumping ability, too.

Other agenda items besides registration are often argued just as rigorously at society meetings. At the 1958 Dartmoor Pony Society Annual General Meeting 'the uproar became so hopeless that the chairman broke up the meeting', and in 1921, after a stormy meeting, many members of the Cleveland Bay Horse Society tore up their membership cards and stormed out in a rage, while at another meeting two members stepped outside to settle their differences, prompting another senior member to declare: 'This is quite like old times. We rarely had a meeting in the old days without someone starting a fight.'

Organizations other than the breed societies have also had a role in influencing breeds. The British Horse Society and its protégé, the Pony Club, which was formed in 1929, have done much to promote better horsemanship and standards, but they may have inadvertently set guidelines which may not have helped British pony breeds. By setting a regime of classifications which matched the rider's age to the height of the pony – which many shows followed for years – the concept of a teenager or small adult riding a pony of 12.2 hands (127 cm) was not catered for, and it

Many riders start their competitive careers on mountain and moorland ponies in lead-rein classes.

The New Forest, like all other native pony breeds, has benefited from the increased competitive opportunities now open to mountain and moorland ponies.

is only relatively recently that the popularity of mountain and moorland classes without a rider age stipulation has rectified this situation and broadened the competitive opportunities for native ponies, with many consequential benefits.

DEMANDS AND INFLUENCES OF HUMAN SOCIETY

For the British horse breeds, it was Man's influence rather than the environment that had the greatest impact. Breeds like the Suffolk Punch, which was selectively bred to be clean-legged to work the soils of the eastern counties, were produced *for* a particular environment rather than *as a result* of it, and they are consequently unlikely to be changed in the short-term by different environments. Their unique qualities will best be retained by working these animals in appropriate occupations – yet the percentage of animals in proper work is now very low. A few breweries keep heavy horses for local deliveries and promotional work, and a few stalwarts still use horsepower on the land for agricultural work although, with a few exceptions, they work *alongside* tractors rather in place of them. In general, their use is more to keep traditions alive and for their owners' pleasure in working alongside horses than for their commercial input. Subsidies for breeding stock would help ensure the survival of these breeds, but maintaining the skills and traditions of working horses is vital if these breeds are not to be merely preserved like museum exhibits.

Keeping old traditions alive – a Fell pony pulling a barge at Foxton Locks, near Market Harborough.

The popularity of ploughing matches, including one for Suffolk Punches only, which, for the public, successfully combine the skills of the working horseman with a sense of nostalgia and tradition, have provided a perfect showcase for the heavy horse breeds and help ensure that they have some functional future outside of the show-ring. Offering the general public the opportunity of working with heavy horses on the land as a recreational activity could mirror the popularity of holidays on working ranches in America while promoting British heavy horse breeds and, tourism being a major rural industry now, there is considerable scope for the use of heavy draught breeds in this field. The Rural Enterprise Scheme which offers grant aid for agricultural diversification projects could perhaps be used to support such projects. Although heavy horses have always been an attraction in heavy trade classes driven to drays, farm waggons and commercial vehicles, in recent years they have

Ploughing matches successfully combine the skills of the horseman and his team with a sense of nostalgia and tradition which appeals to the general public.

200

found a new purpose as riding horses with some even being used for trekking. In America, heavy horses including representatives of the British breeds compete in pulling competitions, which are essentially tests of strength and acceleration, and others demonstrate a speed and manoeuvrability that belies their size and power by competing successfully in speciality barrel-racing classes.

For the Thoroughbred, the popularity of racing worldwide will not only ensure the future of the breed but will also guarantee that its principle attribute of speed will potentially be developed further as the evolutionary process, in this case driven by Man, sees slower animals left out of breeding programmes and only faster animals bred from. In a sense this is a continuation of the natural selection process whereby slower or less resourceful animals were more vulnerable to predators, except in this case only one selection criterion is applied. However, while selective breeding to improve speed alone has seen the size of the English Thoroughbred increase over the years, as a breed it is riddled with hereditary unsoundness. One reason for this is that, since successful racehorses have relatively short racing careers before being retired to stud, any unsoundness problems often do not have time to manifest themselves and are passed, along with their speed, to subsequent generations. There are, of course, exceptions and many Thoroughbreds compete in eventing and other demanding disciplines over long periods without experiencing serious unsoundness problems, but the generalization remains that breeding for one aim alone often has its price to pay.

While the ability to 'perform', in the context of galloping at great speed, is a fundamental requirement of the Thoroughbred, performance in one respect or another – sometimes involving great versatility – is equally important in the other breeds. William Scarth Dixon, writing about British native pony breeds in 1919 commented on 'the immense value of these equine bantams which to the discredit of our countrymen have for so long a time been permitted to languish in the obscurity of unconsidered trifles'. The capabilities of native horse and pony breeds can only be matched by their sheer versatility, and maintaining that performance capability is key to their long-term survival. As Roy B. Charlton, the great pony breeder, once noted: 'This is why the ponies are so good right up to the present day: they have always had to work hard.' Dales, Exmoors, Fells and Highlands have all been used for snigging or extracting the timber from where it had been felled, as a more economical alternative to expensive machinery which necessitates a heavy capital outlay, and most breeds have also worked in a range of agricultural jobs. In the 1930s a Withypool farmer used a pair of Exmoors for ploughing, while at the All Welsh Ploughing Championships in October 1993 one competitor worked a pair of 13 hands (132 cm) Welsh ponies in a full-size plough to prove his comment that 'in the days of horsepower this size of pony was used for all the jobs on many small Welsh farms'. A Dales pony enthusiast even gave a unique demonstration of ploughing with a four-in-hand of Dales ponies to a two-furrow plough at the World Ploughing Championships one year.

Whether it was the Exmoor pony ridden on Home Guard patrol during the Second World War or undertaking postal deliveries in peace time, the Fell pony successfully used as a barge horse in Leicestershire, or the Shetland ponies on stage in the pantomime season, the versatility of British breeds is undeniable. The American showman, William F. Cody (generally better known as Buffalo Bill), who brought his Wild West Show to England to perform in front of Queen Victoria, was sufficiently impressed by Cleveland Bays to purchase a number of pure-breds which he took back to America, and he regularly culminated performances by driving a six-in-hand of Cleveland Bay stallions to a stagecoach. In the early part of the twentieth century a remarkable Highland pony bred by the Duke of Atholl was used in a travelling circus, where he would gallop around the ring carrying acrobats and other performers. According to an observer: 'He concluded his turn by carrying seven full-grown people (five women and two men) at a free and light gallop around the ring. Taking the average weight of the seven riders at eight-and-a-half stones, this pony was carrying at least sixty stones.' Lord Middleham, the noted breeder of Shire horses and Thoroughbreds, used Highlands as grooms' mounts when they 'travelled' the stallions, and Highland ponies are still serving in the army at the Royal Army Veterinary Corps base at Melton Mowbray, where a small number are employed in training personnel in the use and care of pack ponies. Since pony trekking was originally introduced in Scotland in 1952, most breeds have been used successfully in this activity, while in recent years the revival of interest in driving has provided great opportunities again for all breeds. Indeed, it can be said that there is no activity in or out of the show-ring that British native horses and ponies do not excel at, and more recently long-distance riding and other innovative disciplines have provided new opportunities for them to showcase their abilities to a selective and discriminating market.

Highland ponies are still used for training purposes at the Defence Animal Centre at Melton Mowbray.

In evaluating the unique and irreplaceable diversity of British native horse and pony breeds, and the influence they have had on the other equine breeds of the world (which can only be matched by the ubiquitous Arab), it seems incongruous that we should have treated our equine heritage so irresponsibly. Tradition says that if lessons from history are not learnt, history repeats itself, and the loss of so many breeds in the last two hundred years must proportionally increase the value of those breeds we have left and make us more protective of them. In adapting to our needs over the centuries, all these breeds have demonstrated a versatility which should stand them in good stead to meet any future demands that a changing world imposes upon them. We would be poor stewards of this invaluable part of our national heritage if we failed to learn those lessons from the past, to appreciate the diverse characteristics of each breed, publicize their long and challenging histories, conserve and promote them, and ensure their survival for future generations to enjoy.

BREED APPENDICES

Our English horses have all the necessary good properties.
Dr. Fuller, 1662

This section contains details of the currently recognized British breeds of horses and ponies. The descriptions of desirable characteristics of the various breeds (other than the Thoroughbred) are based on information supplied by the National Pony Society and the individual breed societies. The breeds are listed in alphabetical order.

CLEVELAND BAY

A hardy, long-lived and substantial horse with great stamina standing 16–16.2 hands (162.5–167.6 cm), although height should not disqualify an otherwise good sort. Must be bay (that is, with the typical black points – legs, mane and tail), however some grey hairs in mane and tail do not disqualify as these have long been recognized as a feature in certain strains of pure Cleveland blood. White is not admissible, beyond a very small white star. Legs which are bay or red below the knees and hocks do not disqualify, but are faults as to colour. The body should be wide and deep. The back should not be too long, and should be strong, with muscular loins. The shoulders should be sloping, deep and muscular. The quarters should be level, powerful, long and oval, the tail springing well from the quarters. The head should be bold and not too small, and well carried on a long, lean neck. It should have large, kindly eyes and large, fine ears. Forearms and thighs and second thighs should be muscular. The knees and hocks should be large and well closed, and there should be 9 in (23 cm) upwards of good flat bone below the knee, measured at the narrowest point on a tight tape. The pasterns should be strong, sloping and not too long. The legs should be clear of superfluous hair and as clean and hard as possible. One of the most important features of the breed is good feet, which should be blue in colour. Feet that are shallow or narrow are undesirable. The action must be true, straight and free. High action is not characteristic of the breed. The Cleveland which moves well and is full of courage will move freely from the shoulder and will flex the knees and hocks sufficiently. The action required is free all round, gets over the ground, and fits the wear and tear qualities of the breed.

CLYDESDALE

A handsome, weighty and powerful horse, but with a gaiety of carriage and outlook, so that the impression is given of quality and weight, standing 16.2–18 hands (167.6 –183 cm). The most common colours are bay and brown with white markings, but blacks, greys, roans and chestnuts are occasionally seen. The white markings are characteristic and it is the exception to see a bay or brown Clydesdale without a white face and considerable white on the feet and legs. There is a flat profile to the head, broad between the eyes, wide muzzle, large nostrils, a bright, clear, intelligent eye and large ears. The neck is long and well arched, springing out of an oblique shoulder with high withers. The back is short and strong, carrying on towards the rump and this must be associated with lots of spring and depth of rib, like the hoops of a barrel. Quarters are long and well muscled. Forelegs are placed well under the shoulders, and straight from the shoulder to the fetlock joint. There must be no openness at the knees, nor any tendency to knock-knees. Pasterns should be long and set at an angle of 45 degrees from the hoof head to the fetlock joint. Hind legs should be placed well together with the points of the hocks turned inwards rather than outwards. The thighs must come well down to the hocks, and the shanks from the hock to the fetlock joint must be plumb and straight. Feet are open and round. The feather on the legs is a beauty point in the breed and should be silky. Action should be close and true so, when viewed from behind, the foot is lifted clear of the ground at every step. There should be excellent paces and fluidity of movement.

CONNEMARA PONY

Compact, well-balanced riding type with depth, substance and good heart room, standing on short legs covering a lot of ground. Noted for good temperament, hardiness and staying power, intelligence, soundness, surefootedness, and jumping ability. Suitable for either child or adult. Maximum 14.2 hands (147.3 cm) at maturity. Colours grey, black, bay, brown, dun, with occasional roan, chestnut, palomino and dark-eyed cream. Well-balanced pony head of medium length, with good width between large, kindly eyes. Pony ears, well-defined cheekbones, jaw relatively deep but not coarse. Head well set on to neck. Crest should not be over-developed. Neck not set on too low. Well laid-back shoulder giving a good length of rein. Body should be deep, with strong back, some length permissible but should be well ribbed up, with strong loins. Good length and strength in forearms, well-defined knees and short cannons with flat bone measuring 7–8 in (18–20 cm). Elbows should be free. Pasterns of medium length, feet well shaped, of medium size, hard and level. Strong and muscular hindquarters with some length, well developed second thighs (gaskins) and strong low-set hocks. Free, easy and true movement without undue knee action but active and covering the ground.

DALES PONY

A strong, active pony, full of quality and spirit: true pony character, high-couraged, intelligent and kind. A neat, pony-like head, showing no dish: broad between the eyes, which should be bright and alert. Pony ears, slightly incurving. A long forelock of straight hair down the face. Strong neck of ample length – stallions should display a bold outlook with a well-arched crest. Throat and jaws clean-cut. Long, flowing mane. Well-laid, long, sloping shoulders with well-developed muscles. Withers not too fine. Short-coupled body, deep through the chest with well-sprung ribs and deep, lengthy and powerful hindquarters. Second thighs well-developed and very muscular. Tail well set on, not high, with plenty of long, straight hair reaching the ground. Broad, flat hocks well let down, with plenty of dense, flat bone below. Forearms set square, short and very muscular, with broad, well-developed knees. The very best of feet and legs, with flexible joints, showing no coarseness: 8–9 in (20–23 cm) of flat, flinty bone and well-defined tendons. Pasterns should be nicely sloping and of good length. Ample, silky straight feather on the heels. Large, round feet, open at the heels, with well-developed frogs. The preferred height range is 14–14.2 hands (142–147.3 cm): ponies above and below this range to be placed at the discretion of the judge. Colours: Black, brown, a few grey and bay, and occasionally roan. A white star and/or snip on the head; white to the fetlocks of the hind legs only. Mis-marked ponies showing more white than this are registered as section B in the stud book and again placed at the discretion of the judges. Clean, high, straight and true action, going forward on 'all fours' with tremendous energy. The knees and hocks are lifted, the hind legs flexed well under the body for powerful drive.

DARTMOOR PONY

A very good-looking riding pony, sturdily built yet with quality, not exceeding 12.2 hands (127 cm) Colour: bay, black, brown, chestnut, grey and roan. Piebalds and skewbalds are not allowed. Excessive white marking should be discouraged. The head should be small with large, kindly eyes and small alert ears, and a well set on neck of medium length. The throat and jaws should be fine and show no sign of coarseness or throatiness. Stallions to have a moderate crest. Good shoulders are most important and should be well laid-back and sloping but not too fine at the withers. Body of medium length and strong, well ribbed up and with a good depth of girth, giving plenty of heart room. Strong, well-muscled loins and hindquarters, which should be of medium length and neither level nor steeply sloping. The tail should be well set up and, like the mane, full and flowing. The hocks should be well let down, with plenty of length from hip to hock, clean-cut and with plenty of bone below the hock and should neither be sickle nor cow-hocked. There should be a strong second thigh. The forelegs should not be tied in at the elbows, and the forearms should be muscular and relatively long and the knees fairly large and flat on the front. The cannons short with ample, good, flat, flinty bone, and the pasterns sloping but not too long. The feet should be hard and well shaped. There should be low and straight action, coming from the shoulders, with good hock action but without exaggeration.

EXMOOR PONY

Hardy, strong, vigorous and alert with definite 'pony' character. The preferred height range is: stallions and geldings 11.3–12.3 hands (119.4–129.5 cm) at maturity; mares 11.2–12.2 hands (117–127 cm) at maturity. Colours bay, brown or dun, with black points; mealy colour on muzzle around eyes and inside flanks; no white markings anywhere. Summer coat close, hard and bright: winter coat dense, double-layered with an under insulating layer of fine, springy hair and an outer waterproofing layer of hard, greasy hair. Short, thick, pointed ears, clean-cut face, wide forehead, eyes large, wide apart and prominent ('toad eyes'), wide nostrils, clean throat, good length of rein. Shoulders clean, fine at top and well laid back. Deep chest, wide between and behind forelegs, ribs long, deep, well sprung and well apart. Level back, broad and level across loins, tail neatly set in. Clean and short legs with neat, hard feet; forelegs straight, well apart and squarely set; hind legs well apart, nearly perpendicular from hock to fetlock with point of hock in line with pelvis; wide curve from flank to hock point. Straight, smooth action, without exaggeration.

FELL PONY

The Fell pony should constitutionally be as hard as iron and show good pony characteristics with the unmistakable appearance of hardiness peculiar to mountain ponies, and at the same time have a lively and alert appearance and great bone. Height not exceeding 14 hands (142 cm). Colour black, brown, bay or grey. Chestnuts, piebalds and skewbalds are debarred. A star and/or a little white on or below the hind fetlocks is acceptable. An excess of white markings is discouraged, but such ponies are eligible for registration. Small head, well-chiselled in outline, well set on, forehead broad, tapering to nose. Bright, intelligent eyes, small ears. Fine throat and jaws, showing no sign of coarseness. Neck of proportionate length, giving good length of rein, strong and not too heavy; moderate crest in stallion. Well laid back and sloping shoulders, not too fine at withers, nor loaded at the points – a good, long shoulder blade, muscles well developed. Strong back, muscular loins, deep carcase, thick through heart, round-ribbed from shoulders to flank, short and well coupled, hindquarters square and strong with tail well set on. Feet of good size, round and well-formed, open at heels with the characteristic blue horn, pasterns fairly sloping but not too long. Forelegs should be straight, well placed and not tied in at the elbows; big well-formed knees; short cannon bones; plenty of good flat bone below the knee – 8 in (20 cm) at least; great muscularity of arm. Hind legs should display good thighs and second thighs, very muscular; hocks well let down and should not be sickle or cow-hocked; clean cut; plenty of bone below joint. Plenty of fine hair at heels (coarse hair objectionable), all the fine hair except that at the point of heel may be cast in summer. Mane and tail are left to grow long. Action: walk, smart and true; trot well balanced all round with good knee and hock action, going well from the shoulder and flexing the hocks, bringing the hind legs well under the body; not going too wide nor near behind. Should show great 'pace' (length of stride, knee and hock action) and endurance.

HACKNEY HORSE

A stylish harness horse standing 14–15.3 hands (142.2–160 cm). Colours black, brown, bay or chestnut, with or without white markings. A quality head with large, bold eyes set on a neck of moderate length, with more or less crest according to age or sex, and springing from powerful, obliquely sloping shoulders with reasonably high withers. The throat should be fine so that there is no restriction of the air passages when bridling. Body should be of adequate length with well-sprung ribs and of a good depth – a fairly long back is not objectionable in a mare. The upper line of the croup from the loins to the tail should form a convex curve, with the tail well carried. Viewed from the front, the chest should be of ample but not excessive width, while from the rear the quarters and gaskins must be well muscled. The legs should have plenty of clean, flat bone with the tendons clearly defined. Excessive fineness of bone, especially any tendency to be tied in below the knee, is objectionable. The forelegs should be attached well forward, beneath the point of the shoulder. Forearms long and well developed, while the cannon bones should be short and clean with plenty of good flat bone. The pasterns should be sufficiently long and set at the proper oblique angle to give a light, springy step. Forelegs straight without any turning in or out at the pasterns, and no tendency to be 'back' or 'over' at the knees. Hind legs of good length from the stifle to the hock, with short cannon bones. Hocks well formed and not too upright when standing at ease. Hooves well-rounded, in front forming an angle of around 50 degrees with the ground at the toe, rather more upright in the hind hooves. Open at the heels with concave soles. Action straight and true: the front action should be lofty and well-rounded with no tendency to crush the elbows, and the forefeet placed squarely on the ground; the hind legs should be well flexed and brought well under the body with a piston-like action. Dwelling of the hocks in a flexed position is undesirable. Excessive speed is not required but, rather, a pleasing picture of poise and elegance.

HACKNEY PONY

Characteristics similar to the Hackney horse, except that the Hackney pony is expected to show distinct pony characteristics such as small and neat ears; eyes bright, bold and alert; muzzle fine and reasonably small. The body of a Hackney pony can be somewhat more compact than that of the horse, and a height at maturity of 12.2–14 hands (127–142 cm) is characteristic of the breed. The action of a Hackney pony differs from that of a horse in being more brisk but otherwise the main features are similar.

HIGHLAND PONY

A ride, drive and pack pony which can adapt to many equestrian disciplines, standing up to 14.2 hands (147.3 cm). Colour: a range of duns – mouse, yellow, grey, cream, also grey, brown, black and occasionally bay and liver chestnut with silver mane and tail. Many ponies have a dorsal stripe and some show zebra markings on legs and shoulder. A small star is acceptable but other white markings are discouraged. Foal coat often changes and many ponies gradually change colour as they get older, especially those with grey hairs interspersed with the original colour. Others show a slight seasonable change in colour between winter and summer coats. Broken colours are not allowed. Stallions with white markings other than a small star are not eligible for licensing. The head is well carried and alert, with kindly eyes, and broad muzzle with a deep jowl. Reasonable length of neck from withers, with good sloping shoulders and well-placed forearms. Well-balanced and compact body with deep chest with plenty of room for heart and lungs; ribs well sprung. Powerful quarters with well-developed thighs, strong second thighs and clean flat hocks. Limbs showing flat hard bone, broad knees, short cannon bones, oblique pasterns and well-shaped dark, broad hooves. Feather soft and silky; mane and tail naturally flowing and untrimmed, with a full tail. Straight and free movement without undue knee action.

IRISH DRAUGHT

An active, short-legged, powerful horse with substance and quality. Standing over a lot of ground, it has an exceptionally strong and sound constitution, coupled with an intelligent and gentle nature, and is noted for its docility and strength. Stallions stand 15.3–16.3 hands (160–170 cm); mares 15.1–16.1 hands (155–165 cm) approximately. Can be any strong whole colour, including greys, but white above the knees or hocks is not desirable. Good, strong clean bone, which must not be round and coarse. Head should be generous and pleasant, not coarse or hatchet-headed, although a slight Roman nose is permissible. The jawbones should have enough room to take the gullet and allow ease of breathing. Bold eyes set well apart, well-set ears, wide forehead. Clean-cut but not loaded shoulders, withers well-defined, not coarse; the neck set in high and carried proudly. The chest should not be too broad and beefy, the forearms should be long and muscular, not caught in at the elbow; the knees flat and generous, set near the ground; the cannon bones straight and short. The legs should be clean and hard, with a little hair permissible at the back of the fetlocks as necessary protection; the pasterns strong and in proportion, not short and upright nor too weak and long. The hoof should be generous and sound, not boxy or contracted and there should be plenty of room at the heel. The back powerful; the girth very deep; the loins must not be weak (but mares must have enough room to carry the foal). The croup to buttocks to be long and sloping, not short and rounded or flat-topped; hips not wide and plain; thighs strong and powerful and at least as wide from the back view as the hips; the second thighs long and well developed; the hocks near the ground and generous, points not too close together or wide apart but straight, and they should not be out behind the horse nor should they be over-bent or in any way weak. Cannon bones short and strong. Smooth and free action but without exaggeration, and not heavy or ponderous. Walk and trot to be straight and true with good flexion in the hocks and freedom of the shoulders

NEW FOREST PONY

New Forest ponies should be of working type, with substance. They should have sloping shoulders, strong quarters, plenty of flat bone, good depth of body, straight limbs and good, hard, round feet. The ponies are generally quite capable of carrying adults, while narrow enough for small children. The smaller ponies, although not up to so much weight, often show more quality. The upper limit is 14.2 hands (147.3 cm), there being no lower limit. All ponies should be judged equally regardless of height. However, they are normally shown in two height sections: 13.2 hands (137 cm) and under, and over 13.2 hands (more than 137 cm). New Forest ponies may be any colour except piebald, skewbald, spotted and blue-eyed cream. Since 2004, palomino or very light chestnut and cream ponies with dark eyes have not been eligible as licensed stallions. Blue eyes are not permitted. White markings on the head and legs are permitted except that: '*A pony shall not have any white markings on pink skin behind the head, above a horizontal line level with the bony protuberance of the accessory carpal bone at the back of the knee in the forelimb and the point of the hock in the hind limb.*' Action should be free, active and straight, but not exaggerated. The New Forest pony has an ideal temperament and should be very easy to train.

SHETLAND PONY

A most salient and essential feature of the Shetland pony is its general air of vitality (presence), stamina and robustness. Shetlands are traditionally measured not in hands, but inches and registered stock must not exceed 40 in (101.6 cm) at three years or under, nor 42 in (106.7 cm) at four years or over. Shetland ponies may be any colour known in horses except spotted. The coat changes according to the seasons; a double coat in winter with guard hairs which shed the rain and keep the pony's skin completely dry in the worst of weather and, by contrast, a short summer coat which should carry a beautiful silky sheen. At all times the mane and tail should be long, straight and profuse and the feathering of the fetlocks straight and silky. The head should be small, carried well and in proportion. Ears should be small and erect, wide set but pointing well forward. Forehead should be broad with bold, dark, intelligent eyes. Muzzle must be broad with nostrils wide and open. Teeth and jaw must be correct (i.e. no deformities such as overshot or undershot mouth). The neck should be properly set onto the shoulder, which in turn should be sloping, not upright, and end in well defined withers. The body should be strong with plenty of heart room, well-sprung ribs, the loins strong and muscular. The quarters should be broad and long with the tail set well up on them. Forelegs should be well-placed with sufficient good, flat bone, strong forearm, short, balanced cannon bone, and springy pasterns. The hindquarters should be strong and muscular with well-shaped strong hocks and, when viewed from behind, the hind legs should not be set too widely apart, nor should the hocks be turned in. Tough, round and well shaped feet – not too short, narrow, contracted or thin. Straight, free action using every joint and tracking up well.

SHIRE

A powerful, active draught horse standing 16 hands (162.5 cm) upwards for mares, 16.2 hands (167.6 cm) upwards for geldings and 17 hands (173 cm) average for stallions at maturity, with many standing around 17.2 hands (178 cm). Colours black, brown, bay or grey for stallions; plus roans for mares or geldings. Stallions should preferably not be splashed with large white patches over the body, and they must not be roan or chestnut (so any male born these colours must be gelded in order to be registered). Long and lean head, neither too large nor too small. A large jawbone should be avoided. Large eyes, well set and docile in expression. Wall eyes are not allowed in stallions and are only acceptable in grade A and B register mares. Slightly Roman nose, nostrils thin and wide, lips together (not pendulous). Long, lean, sharp and sensitive ears. Clean-cut and lean throat. Deep and oblique shoulders, wide enough to support the collar. Long, slightly arched neck, well set on to give the horse a commanding appearance. The girth varies from 6 ft to 8ft (183–244 cm) in stallions of from 16.2 to 18 hands

(167.6–183 cm), less for mares and geldings depending on the size and age of the animal. Short back, strong and muscular, often longer in mares, which should not be dipped or roached. Loins standing well up, denoting good constitution (must not be flat). Broad across the chest, with legs well under the body and well-enveloped in muscle, otherwise action is impeded. Long and sweeping hindquarters, wide and full of muscle, well let down towards the thighs. Round, deep and well-sprung ribs, not flat. Forelegs should be as straight as possible down to the pasterns; hocks should not be too far back and should be in line with the hindquarters, with ample width broadside and narrow in front. 'Puffy' and 'sickle' hocks should be avoided. The leg sinews should be clean-cut and hard, like fine cords to the touch, and clear of short cannon bones; 11 in (28 cm) of flat bone is ample, sometimes a little less in mares, although occasionally 12$\frac{1}{2}$ in (31.8 cm) is recorded in stallions. Deep, solid and wide hooves with thick, open walls. Straight and true action in front and behind, going with force using both knees and hocks, the latter being kept close together.

SUFFOLK PUNCH

A short-legged, powerful horse. Although the standard for the breed has never included a height stipulation, preferred heights are up to 16.2 hands (167.6 cm) for a mare and up to 17.1 hands (175.3 cm) for a stallion. Colour is always chestnut, although seven shades are recognized: bright, red, golden, yellow, light, dark and dull dark. A few white hairs well-mixed with the chestnut on the body, and a star, stripe or a little white on the forehead is no detriment. The head should be large, with a broad forehead. Neck muscular and deep where the collar lies, tapering gracefully towards the head. Deep, round-ribbed body set on short legs, giving rise to its popular name of 'punch'. The back is short and, unlike the Clydesdale, the Suffolk should have great width across the chest and in the quarters. The shoulders should be long, muscular and sloping. The short legs, which consequently place the powerful body closer to the ground, giving a more direct line of draught than the other heavy breeds, should be straight, with up to 11 in (28 cm) of bone in some examples, with sloping pasterns, large, clean joints and no coarse hair, culminating in large, well-shaped hooves. The action is well-balanced and straight.

THOROUGHBRED

Everything about the Thoroughbred should suggest refinement and speed. The height varies between 15 and 17 hands (152.5–173 cm) and the usual colours are black, bay, brown, chestnut or grey. Roans are rarely seen, but white markings on the face and legs are common. The head is small and elegant with a straight profile and set on a long, slightly arched neck set into well laid-back shoulders with pronounced withers. The body should be short-backed and deep with a well-sprung ribcage to allow plenty of lung room. The hindquarters are long and muscular with well let down hocks, and the limbs are long, clean and hard, with plenty of bone, well-defined tendons and long, sloping pasterns. The action is long-striding and free.

WELSH SECTION A PONY

Hardy, spirited and pony-like, not exceeding 12 hands (122 cm) and any colour except piebald or skewbald. Small, clean-cut head, well set on and tapering to the muzzle. Bold eyes. Small, pointed ears, proportionately close. Clean and 'finely cut' throat, with ample room at the angle of the jaw. Lengthy neck, well carried and moderately lean in the case of mares, but inclined to be cresty in the case of mature stallions. Long, sloping shoulders, withers moderately fine, but not 'knifey'. The humerus upright, so that the foreleg is not set in under the body. Forelegs set square and true, and not tied in at the elbows. Long, strong forearms, well-developed knees, short flat bone below knee, pasterns of proportionate slope and length, feet well-shaped with round, dense hooves. Back and loins muscular, strong and well coupled. Deep girth with well-sprung ribs. Hocks to be large, flat and clean with points prominent, turning neither inwards nor outwards. The hind leg not to be too bent. The hock not to be set behind a line from the point of the quarter to the fetlock joint. Hind pasterns and feet to have same general characteristics as those of forelimbs. Quick, free action straight from the shoulder; knees and hocks well flexed with straight and powerful leverage and well under the body.

WELSH SECTION B PONY

The general description of ponies in Section A of the stud book (given above) is applicable to those in Section B, but more particularly the Section B pony shall be described as a riding pony with quality, riding action, adequate bone and substance, hardiness and constitution and with pony character, not exceeding 13.2 hands (137 cm).

WELSH SECTION C AND D COBS

Strong, hardy and active, with pony character and as much substance as possible. Section C not exceeding 13.2 hands (137 cm), and Section D exceeding this height but with no upper limit. Any colour, except piebald or skewbald. The head full of quality and pony character; a coarse head and Roman nose are most objectionable. Bold, prominent eyes. Neat ears. Lengthy neck, well carried and moderately lean in the case of mares, but inclined to be cresty in the case of mature stallions. Strong, well laid back shoulders. Forelegs set square and not tied in at the elbows. Long, strong forearms. Knees well-developed with an abundance of bone below them. Pasterns of proportionate slope and length. Feet well-shaped; hooves dense. When in the rough, a moderate quantity of silky hair is not objected to, but coarse, wiry hair is a definite objection. Back and loins muscular, strong and well coupled. Deep through the heart and well ribbed up. Lengthy and strong hindquarters; ragged or drooping quarters are objectionable. Tail well set on. Second thighs strong and muscular. Hocks, large flat and clean, with points prominent, turning neither inwards nor outwards. The hind legs must not be too bent and the hocks not set behind a line falling from the point of the quarters to the fetlock joints. Hind pasterns and feet to have same general characteristics as those of forelimbs. Free, true and 'forcible' action with the knee bent and the whole foreleg extended straight from the shoulder and as far forward as possible in the trot. Hocks flexed under the body with straight and powerful leverage.

INDEX

Index